Buckle Down™

Reading

Level 2

2nd Edition

This book belongs to: _____

Buckle Down
P u b l i s h i n g

Helping your schoolhouse meet the standards of the statehouse™

Acknowledgments

"The Unhappy Donkey," a fable by Aesop, adapted by Alan Noble.

"Rosy," a Cinderella story from Egypt, as retold by Alicia Monroe.

"Tam," a Cinderella story from Vietnam, as retold by Rick Zollo.

"Choosing Shoes" from *The Very Thing* by Ffrida Wolfe, copyright © 1928 by Sidgwick & Jackson, Ltd. Reprinted by permission of Macmillan Publishers, Ltd.

Peanuts reprinted by permission of United Feature Syndicate, Inc.

Charles Schulz photo reprinted courtesy of United Feature Syndicate, Inc.

Every effort has been made by the publisher to locate each owner of the copyrighted material reprinted in this publication and to secure the necessary permissions. If there are any questions regarding the use of these materials, the publisher will take appropriate corrective measures to acknowledge ownership in future publications.

ISBN 0-7836-5775-7

2BDUS02RD01   1 2 3 4 5 6 7 8 9 10

Senior Editor: Nick Caster; Project Editor: Renée Rogers; Editor: Susan McCarty; Production Editor: Jennifer Rapp; Cover Design: Christina Nantz; Cover Graphic Designer: Christina Kroemer; Production Director: Jennifer Booth; Art Director: Chris Wolf; Graphic Designers: Mark Nodland, Kelli Rossetti; Composition: Wyndham Books.

Cover image: © Bob Garas/Inspirestock/Jupiterimages

TABLE OF CONTENTS

Table of Contents

To the Teacher:

Standards and Skills codes are listed for each lesson in the table of contents and for each page in the shaded gray bars that run across the tops of the pages in the workbook (see the example at right). These codes identify the Standards and Skills covered on a given page.

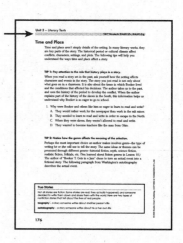

Introduction

Buckle Down Reading, Level 2, was written for kids just like you. It has stories that are true and stories that are made up. You'll read about strange pets, best friends, and what life was like for Abraham Lincoln when he was very young. You'll also learn to read graphs and follow directions.

This book will help you practice spelling, too. There's even a Word Power Log beginning on page 168. Use it to help you learn new words and how to spell them.

Each lesson will ask you questions about what you have read. These questions will ask you to choose the best answer or write an answer of your own. You will also get to do these things to help you learn:

- draw a picture
- cut and paste pictures
- do a dot-to-dot

This workbook will help you understand and remember things you learn about reading in school. It will also give you practice for taking a reading test.

Test-Taking Tips

 TIP 1: Read the directions carefully.

Read all the directions with care. Listen carefully to any directions your teacher reads to you or tells you. If there is anything you do not understand, ask your teacher to explain it.

 TIP 2: Read stories carefully.

Read each story all the way through before answering any questions.

 TIP 3: Read questions and answer choices carefully.

Make sure you read through all of the answer choices before choosing one. Choice A may look good, but Choice C may look better.

 TIP 4: Make sure your answer is based on what the story says.

Questions on a reading test are about things the story tells you. The correct answer will always be about ideas from the story.

 TIP 5: Use key words in the question. They will help you find answers in the story.

Key words in a question can point to where the answer will be found in the story. Find an important word in the question, then go back and look for that word in the story. When you find that word, you will probably find the correct answer. You will learn more about using key words in Lesson 5 of this book.

 TIP 6: Don't let hard questions scare you.

Some questions will be easy to answer. Some questions will be hard to answer. Think about what the question is asking. If the question is too hard, skip it and go on to the next one. Come back to the question later. If you still don't know the answer, take a guess!

TIP 7: Answer every question, even if you have to guess.

If you don't know the answer to a test question, guess. Cross out any answers that you know are wrong, then pick from those that are left. Remember, if you don't answer a question you can't get it right.

 TIP 8: When asked to write an answer, write neatly.

Some questions will ask you to write a word, a sentence, or more. When you are asked to write an answer, be sure to use your best handwriting.

 TIP 9: On test day, stay cool!

Take it easy on test day. You probably know more than you think you know. If you have studied every lesson in this book, you will have the test-taking tools you need to do your very best.

Unit 1

Understanding Words

Can a book talk to you? It can if you know how to read the words. When you read, the words are talking to you as you sound them out.

In this unit, you will learn many ways to play with words. You will learn how to break words into sound parts. You will also see words that are like each other and words that are different.

This unit will show you ways to make reading easier.

So, listen to this book. It's talking to you!

Lesson 1: Word Sounds

Did you know there are names for the kinds of letters in the alphabet? The letters in the alphabet are called vowels and consonants. The **vowels** are the letters *a, e, i, o,* and *u.* The **consonants** are all of the other letters.

 TIP 1: Syllables are the different sound parts in a word.

Syllables are the different sound parts in a word. Some words have one syllable. Some words have two syllables. Some words have even more syllables than that.

Learn how to count syllables. First, put one of your fingers under your chin. Put it close to your chin but not touching it.

Now say the word *cat.* Count how many times your chin hits your finger. That is how many syllables in a word. Did your chin hit your finger one time? The word *cat* has one syllable.

1. How many syllables does the word *splash* have?

   A. 1

   B. 2

   C. 3

2. How many syllables does the word *grandmother* have?

   A. 1

   B. 2

   C. 3

TIP 2: Words are easier to read and spell when you break them up.

When reading or spelling a hard word, break it up into syllables. Words are easier to say and spell when you break them into smaller parts.

Some syllables end by making a vowel sound. Look at these words:

    ma / ma   pa / pa   mo / vie   a / gree

3. Which of these sound parts ends with a vowel sound?

    A. er

    B. da

    C. ten

Other syllables end with a consonant sound. Look at these words:

    al / most   cor / ner   for / ev / er   en / ter

4. Which of these sound parts ends with a consonant sound?

    A. ner

    B. tie

    C. mo

Here are some words with different sound parts. Some syllables end with vowel sounds. Others end with consonant sounds:

    ta / ken   a / part / ment   re / mem / ber

    un / tie   be / tween   news / pa / per

5. Which of these words has one syllable that ends with a vowel sound, and another that ends with a consonant sound?

    A. bet / ter

    B. din / ner

    C. be / gin

TIP 3: Consonants can make hard sounds or soft sounds.

Some consonants can make a hard sound or a soft sound. A **hard sound** is like the *c* in *cup* or the *g* in *green*. A **soft sound** is like the first *c* in *circus* or the *g* in *gentle*.

6. Write the word that fits best below each picture.

    Both of these animal names start with a hard-*c* sound.

_____   _____

Both of these animal names start with a hard-*g* sound.

_____   _____

Both of these words start with a hard-*c* sound.

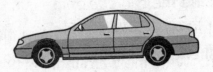

_____   _____

The first word starts with a soft-*c* sound. The second word ends with a soft-*c* sound.

_____   _____

Look at the words in Numbers 7 through 11. One letter is darker than the others. If the dark letter makes a hard sound, circle *Hard*. If the dark letter makes a soft sound, circle *Soft*. We did the first one for you.

7. **c**ap   (Hard)   Soft

8. **c**an   Hard   Soft

9. **c**ircle   Hard   Soft

10. **g**old   Hard   Soft

11. **g**iant   Hard   Soft

TIP 4: Vowels can make long sounds or short sounds.

Vowels can make two sounds. A **long-vowel sound** is when a vowel says its name.

The vowel says its name in the word *day*. When you say your ABCs, the letter *a* has the same sound as it does in the word *day*. The letter *a* has a long-vowel sound in the word *day*.

A **short-vowel sound** is when a vowel makes a sound that is not like its name. In the word *hat*, the vowel makes a sound that is not like its name. The letter *a* has a short-vowel sound in the word *hat*.

 TIP 5: A vowel with one or more consonants after it has a short-vowel sound most of the time.

A vowel with one or more consonants after it has a short-vowel sound most of the time.

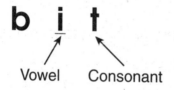

Look at these words:

lid   **up**   **app**le   **hop**   **egg**

12. Write another word that has a short-vowel sound.

_____

13. Does the word *lock* have a long-*o* or a short-*o* sound?

_____

TIP 6: A vowel with a consonant and a final *e* after it makes a long sound.

A vowel with a consonant and a final *e* after it makes a long sound.
A **final *e*** is an *e* at the end of the word. The *e* at the end makes no sound.

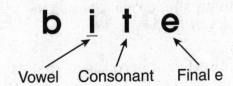

Look at these words:

n**ame**   ins**ide**   c**ave**   r**ule**   f**ace**

14. Write another word that has a long vowel sound.

_____

15. Does the word *camp* have a long-*a* or a short-*a* sound?

_____

 TIP 7: A vowel with the letters *dge* after it makes a short sound.

A vowel with the letters *dge* after it makes a short sound.

TIP 8: A vowel with the letters *ge* after it makes a long sound.

A vowel with the letters *ge* after it makes a long sound.

Long Sound

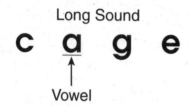

Vowel

Look at these words:

short vowels: badge   judge

long vowels: age   huge

16. Does the word *page* have a long-*a* or a short-*a* sound?

_____

 TIP 9: When two vowels are side by side in a word, you hear only the first vowel.

Vowels are next to each other in many words. In the word *beak*, the vowels *e* and *a* are next to each other.

When two vowels are next to each other, the first vowel has a long sound. That's the one you hear. The second vowel is silent.

Just remember:

When two vowels go walking,
The first one does the talking.

Look at these words:

blue   sea   leap   tie   toast

17. Think of another word that follows this rule. Write the word on the line.

_____

18. Do the letters *ea* in the word *cream* have a long-*a* or a long-*e* sound?

_____

 TIP 10: When there is one vowel at the end of a word, the vowel has a long sound.

Look at these words:

    sh**e**   n**o**   h**i**   b**e**   m**e**

19. Write another word that has a vowel with a long sound at the end.

_____

20. Does the word *so* have a long-*o* or a short-*o* sound?

_____

 TIP 11: The letter *r* tells you how some words sound.

When you see a vowel that is followed by the letter *r*, be careful. There are three sounds that can be made when the letter *r* comes after a vowel. These sounds are:

    ar   c**ar**, b**ar**k, st**ar**t

    or   b**or**n, w**ar**m, f**or**

    er   wat**er**, d**ir**t, w**or**m

21. Write another word that ends in a consonant and has the letter *r* after a vowel.

_____

Reading Practice

1. Which word begins with a soft-*c* sound?

   Ⓐ cap

   Ⓑ city

   Ⓒ carrot

2. Which word has a long-*a* vowel sound?

   Ⓐ brave

   Ⓑ apple

   Ⓒ chance

3. Which word has the same sound as *ee* in the word *seen*?

   Ⓐ bed

   Ⓑ bell

   Ⓒ bean

4. Which word has the same sound as the *st* in the word *stone*?

   Ⓐ smart

   Ⓑ must

   Ⓒ float

5. How many syllables are there in the word *elephant*?

   Ⓐ one

   Ⓑ two

   Ⓒ three

6. How many syllables are there in the word *chipmunk*?

   Ⓐ one

   Ⓑ two

   Ⓒ three

Lesson 2: Putting Letters Together

Groups of letters can make sounds in different ways. This lesson will teach you about the sounds that letters make together.

 TIP 1: In some words, each letter says its sound in order.

Sometimes you can hear each letter, one at a time. In these examples, each letter is heard by itself before the next letter is heard.

    cot   cat   pin   men   mug

In the word *cot*, you can hear the sound of each letter, one after another.

    c + o + t

The same is true with the word *cat*.

    c + a + t

If we take away the *c* from the word *cat*, the new word becomes *at*. The new word has only two letter sounds.

    a + t

And, if we switch the first and last letters in *gum*, we get a new word. That word is *mug*.

    g + u + m

    becomes

    m + u + g

TIP 2: Two letters can put their sounds together.

Sometimes two or more letters can put their sounds together. Look at these words:

    blue   **t**ree   **cr**ash

In the word *blue*, the sound of the *b* and the sound of the *l* mix together. They make the sound *bl*.

In the word *tree*, the sound of the *t* goes together with the sound of the *r*. They make the sound *tr*.

In the word *crash*, the sound of the *c* goes together with the sound of the *r* to make the sound *cr*.

 TIP 3: Two or more letters can make a new sound.

Sometimes the letters do not put their sounds together. They make a new sound, like the **ch** in **cheese**. Here are some other letters that make new sounds when they are put together:

    sh as in the word **shoe**   *tch* as in the word *watch*

    th as in the word **throw**   *gh* as in the word *enough*

Read the following words. If the dark letters put their sounds together, circle *Together*. If the dark letters make a new sound, circle *New Sound*. We did the first one for you.

1. **bl**ack   (Together)   New Sound

2. lau**gh**   Together   New Sound

3. mu**st**   Together   New Sound

4. **th**em   Together   New Sound

5. **gr**ow   Together   New Sound

6. ca**tch**   Together   New Sound

TIP 4: Two vowels side by side make one sound.

In Lesson 1, you learned that vowels are the letters *a, e, i, o,* and *u.* Two vowels written together can make one sound.

Look at this list of examples:

ai as in *tail*

au as in *caught*

ea as in *peach*

ee as in *week*

ei as in *receive*

ie as in *tie*

oa as in *goat*

oo as in *boot* or *oo* as in *book*

ui as in *fruit*

Sometimes, two different sets of vowels can make the same sounds. Look at the words *week* and *peach* above. The letters *ee* and *ea* make the same vowel sound.

7. Which word has the same vowel sound as the word *leaf*?

   A. let

   B. life

   C. meet

8. Which word has the same vowel sound as the word *boat*?

   A. note

   B. poor

   C. boss

TIP 5: Two words can have the same vowels but make different vowel sounds.

Look at the words *boot* and *book*. They use the same vowels but make different sounds. Here are some other words that use the same vowels but make different sounds. Listen to the difference as your teacher reads these words out loud.

most	**lost**
low	**wow**

The best way to learn how to say and spell these words is to practice. Words are tricky. Sometimes they follow rules. Sometimes they don't. But if you're careful, you'll learn which words follow rules, and which words don't.

 TIP 6: Words in a word family have the same kind of spelling.

A **word family** is a group of words that have the same kind of spelling. That means that the beginnings, middles, or ends of the words are spelled the same. For example, the words *bake*, *cake*, *lake*, and *snake* are in the same word family because they all use the letters *ake*.

On the next page, you will see some word families that you should know. Read the first two words in each group. Then fill in the letters to make a third word in the same family. Each box has a picture to help you find out what the third word is. The first one has been done for you.

ast

last

fast

c ast _____

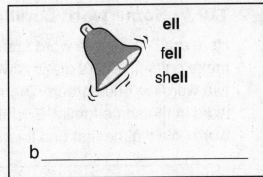

ell

f**ell**

sh**ell**

b _____

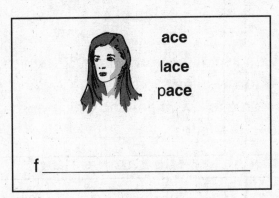

ace

l**ace**

p**ace**

f _____

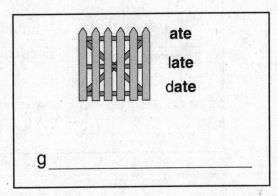

ate

l**ate**

d**ate**

g _____

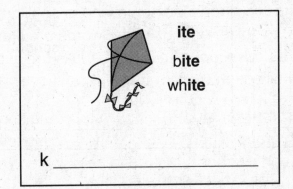

ite

b**ite**

wh**ite**

k _____

ive

f**ive**

l**ive**

d _____

ore

st**ore**

m**ore**

c _____

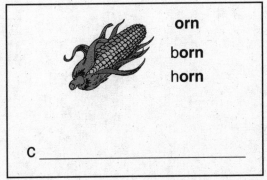

orn

b**orn**

h**orn**

c _____

TIP 7: Some word families have special pairs of letters.

Here are some more word families that have special pairs of letters. When these pairs of letters are in a word, they make a new sound. Read the first two words in each group. Then fill in the correct letters to make a third word in the same family. Each box has a picture to help you make the new word. We did the first one for you.

au

hau**l**

be**cau**se

_____ au to

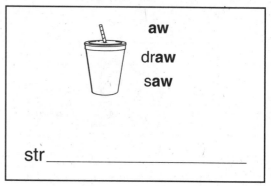

aw

dr**aw**

s**aw**

str_____

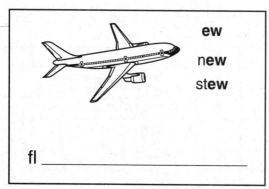

ew

n**ew**

st**ew**

fl_____

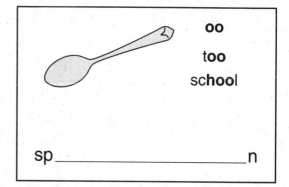

oo

t**oo**

sch**oo**l

sp_____n

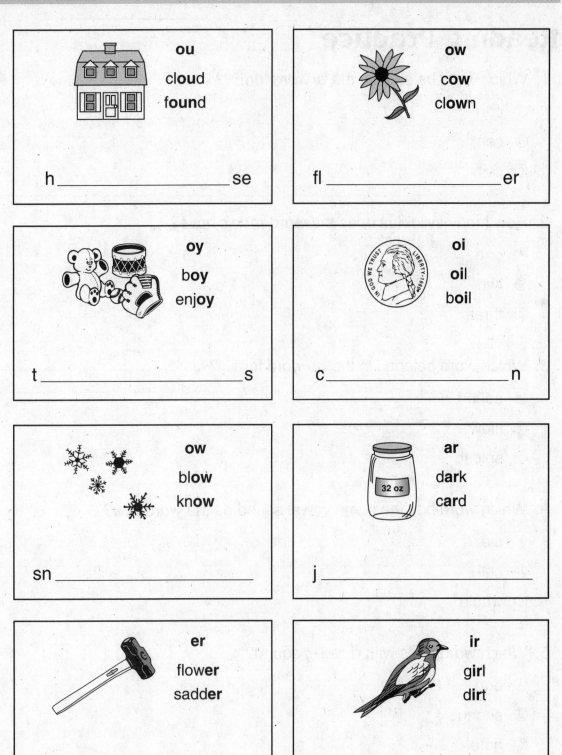

ou

cloud

found

h _____ se

ow

cow

clown

fl _____ er

oy

boy

enjoy

t _____ s

oi

oil

boil

c _____ n

ow

blow

know

sn _____

ar

dark

card

j _____

er

flower

sadder

hamm _____

ir

girl

dirt

b _____ d

Reading Practice

1. Which word belongs in the *oi* word family?

    Ⓐ can

    Ⓑ cent

    Ⓒ coin

2. How many syllables does the word *magic* have?

    Ⓐ one

    Ⓑ two

    Ⓒ three

3. Which word belongs in the *ou* word family?

    Ⓐ sound

    Ⓑ slow

    Ⓒ splash

4. Which word has the same vowel sound as the word *pail*?

    Ⓐ tile

    Ⓑ call

    Ⓒ whale

5. Which word ends with a soft-*g* sound?

    Ⓐ egg

    Ⓑ change

    Ⓒ gate

6. Which set of dark letters makes a new sound?

    Ⓐ **bl**ue

    Ⓑ **ch**ase

    Ⓒ **dr**eam

Lesson 3: Spelling

Did you know spelling can be fun? It's kind of like a game. When you play a new game, it can seem hard. But once you know all the rules, it's very fun. Spelling is the same way. This lesson will help you learn the rules.

 TIP 1: Words can be singular or plural.

A **singular** word stands for one thing. *Button*, *monkey*, and *child* are singular words.

A **plural** word stands for two or more things. *Buttons*, *monkeys*, and *children* are plural words.

 TIP 2: Add an *s* to singular words to make them plural.

Most singular words can be changed to plural words by adding an *s*. Look at this example:

one kite   four kites

Make the following words plural:

1. cat

   _____

2. tree

   _____

TIP 3: Add an *es* to some words to make them plural.

Some singular words end in the letters *s, ss, sh, ch,* or *x.* These words can be made plural by adding *es.* Look at these examples:

gas	gasses
mess	messes
wish	wishes
branch	branches
box	boxes

Make the following words plural:

3. kiss

_____

4. lunch

_____

5. dish

_____

 TIP 4: Change a *y* to *i* and add *es* to make some words plural.

Sometimes a singular word ends with a consonant followed by *y.* To make this kind of word plural, change the *y* to *i.* Then add *es.* Look at this example:

family	famil**ies**

Make the following words plural:

6. fly

_____

7. lady

_____

8. worry

_____

Here are a few more practice words. Write each one as a plural.

9. ranch

_____

10. ship

_____

11. baby

_____

12. beach

_____

13. bush

_____

TIP 5: Some words show belonging.

Sometimes you write to show that something belongs to something or someone else. Most of the time, you add the mark ' and the letter *s* to singular words.

Look at these examples:

Singular

The owl that belongs to Tim is **Tim's owl**.

Add the mark ' to plural words that end in *s*.

Plurals that end in *s*

The school that the boys go to is **the boys' school**.

Rewrite the following words by adding '*s* or '. The first one has been done for you.

14. The balloons that belong to the clowns are the

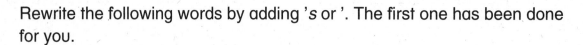
clowns' balloons.

15. The bone that belongs to the dog is the

16. The pennies that belong to the child are the

TIP 6: Some plural words have different endings.

Some words cannot be made plural by adding an *s*, *es*, or *ies* at the end. The best way to find out how to make a word plural is to look in a dictionary. Here are some tricky plurals you should know.

Singular	Plural	Singular	Plural
child	children	mouse	mice
deer	deer	man	men
foot	feet	woman	women

Make the following words plural. You may use a dictionary to help.

17. goose

_____

18. sheep

_____

19. tooth

_____

Reading Practice

1. Which word is the plural for the word *dog*?

   Ⓐ dog

   Ⓑ dogs

   Ⓒ doges

2. Which word is the plural for the word *fox*?

   Ⓐ fox

   Ⓑ foxs

   Ⓒ foxes

3. Which word has the same vowel sound as the word *gold*?

   Ⓐ coal

   Ⓑ card

   Ⓒ care

4. Which word is the plural for the word *cherry*?

   Ⓐ cherrys

   Ⓑ cherryes

   Ⓒ cherries

5. Which words show that the basketball belongs to Joe?

   Ⓐ Joe's basketball

   Ⓑ Joes basketball

   Ⓒ Joes' basketball

6. Which word is the same for the plural and the singular?

   Ⓐ sheep

   Ⓑ goose

   Ⓒ teeth

7. Which words show that the coins belong to the girls?

   Ⓐ the girl's coins

   Ⓑ the girls coins

   Ⓒ the girls' coins

Lesson 4: Word Play

You can play with the words you know to make new words. You can put two words together. You can add letters to the beginning or the end of a word. You'll learn about these ways of making new words in this lesson.

 TIP 1: You can make new words by putting two words together.

Many new words can be made by putting two shorter words together. For example, the word *goldfish* is made up of the words *gold* and *fish*. Look at these other examples:

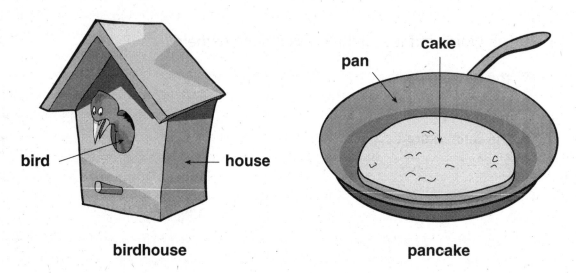

bird — house

birdhouse

pan / cake

pancake

Put two words together to make new words. The first one has been done for you.

1. can + not

   cannot

2. down + town

3. every + thing

4. Which of these is two words put together?

   A. moonlight

   B. television

   C. remember

5. Which of these is two words put together?

   A. feather

   B. elephant

   C. bedroom

6. Which of these is two words put together?

   A. monkey

   B. daylight

   C. message

Look at the pictures. Write what each picture shows. Each picture is something made from two words put together. We did the first one for you.

classroom

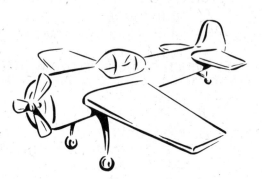

_____

_____

_____

_____

TIP 2: You can make a new word by adding letters to the beginning of a word.

You can make a new word by adding letters to the beginning of a word. A **prefix** is one or more letters added to the beginning of a word.

Each prefix has its own meaning. The letters *un-* make a prefix. *Un-* means not. When you add *un-* to the word *able*, you can make a new word. The new word is *unable*. This new word means "not able."

    un + able = unable

Here are some more prefixes and what they mean:

    re-   again
    pre-   before
    mis-   wrong
    over-   too much

For Numbers 7 through 10, write the new word. We did the first one for you.

7. re + play = _replay_

8. pre + cook = _____

9. mis + spell = _____

10. over + tired = _____

TIP 3: A root word is the word you add letters to.

A **root word** is the word you add letters to. Adding a prefix will change the meaning of the root word.

11. What is the root word in the word *rerun*?

_____

12. What is the root word in the word *untold*?

_____

Try writing new words by putting together prefixes and root words.

13. Write a word that means "paint again."

_____

14. Write a word that means "not clean."

_____

15. Write a word that means to "fill too much."

_____

16. Write a word that means "mix before."

_____

 TIP 4: You can make a new word by adding letters to the end of a word.

A **suffix** is one or more letters added to the end of a word. Adding a suffix changes the meaning of a root word.

Each suffix has its own meaning. The letters *-est* are a suffix. *The suffix -est* means *most*. When you add *-est* to the word *green*, you can make a new word. The new word is *greenest*. This new word means "the most green."

green + est = greenest

Here are some more suffixes and what they mean:

-er   more

-ful   full of

-ly   in this way

-ing   doing something

-less   not having something

Try writing new words by putting together root words and suffixes. We did the first one for you.

17. Write a word that means "more old."

   older

18. Write a word that means "most tall."

   _____

19. Write a word that means "full of hope."

   _____

20. Write a word that means "more fast."

   _____

21. Write a word that means "taking a walk."

   _____

TIP 5: Some words have a suffix and a prefix.

Some words have a suffix and a prefix. To find out what these words mean, find the root word first. Then find the prefix and the suffix.

22. Which word has a suffix and a prefix?

   A. rethrow

   B. softly

   C. prewashing

Reading Practice

1. Which of these is two words put together?

   Ⓐ mountain

   Ⓑ weekend

   Ⓒ teacher

2. Which word means to "try again"?

   Ⓐ mistry

   Ⓑ trying

   Ⓒ retry

3. Which of these is two words put together?

   Ⓐ afternoon

   Ⓑ chimney

   Ⓒ important

4. Which word means "not having sound"?

   Ⓐ sounding

   Ⓑ soundless

   Ⓒ sounder

5. Which of these is two words put together?

   Ⓐ evening

   Ⓑ donkey

   Ⓒ something

6. How many syllables does the word *important* have?

    Ⓐ one

    Ⓑ two

    Ⓒ three

7. Which word means to "count wrongly"?

    Ⓐ recount

    Ⓑ miscount

    Ⓒ countless

8. Which set of dark letters makes a new sound?

    Ⓐ **sh**ook

    Ⓑ **st**airs

    Ⓒ **fl**ash

Lesson 5: The Same and Different

Words can be tricky, but they can be fun, too. In this lesson, you'll learn about pairs of words that mean the same thing. You'll also learn about pairs of words that mean different things. Then you'll learn more about the different sounds of words.

 TIP 1: Synonyms are words that mean the same thing.

Sometimes you'll find two words that mean the same thing. **Synonyms** are words that mean the same thing. *Happy* and *glad* mean the same thing.

Read each pair of sentences. Draw a circle around the words from both sentences that have the same meaning. We did the first pair for you.

1. Mary is the team's (quickest) runner.

   She always runs the (fastest).

2. When does my favorite show begin?

   It will start at 8 o'clock.

3. Mike has a very small dog.

   Kareem's dog is little, too.

4. Are you able to reach the cookie jar?

   I can run almost as fast as my brother.

TIP 2: Opposites are words that mean very different things.

Most words mean different things. But **opposites** are sets of words that mean very different things. *Clean* and *dirty* are opposites. *Open* and *closed* are also opposites. Opposites can be called **antonyms**.

Read each pair of sentences. Draw a circle around the words from both sentences that have the opposite meanings. We did the first pair for you.

5. The butter was as (hard) as a rock.

   The ice cream was (soft).

6. My father works during the day.

   Tim's father works at night.

7. That store opens at 9 o'clock.

   This store never closes.

8. My glass is empty.

   Your glass is full.

> **TIP 3: Some words mean more than one thing.**

Many words have more than one meaning. A bat is what you use to play baseball. A bat is also a small animal that flies at night.

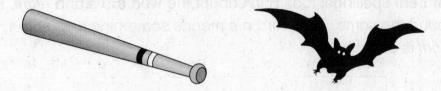

9. Write the word that goes with both pictures on the line.

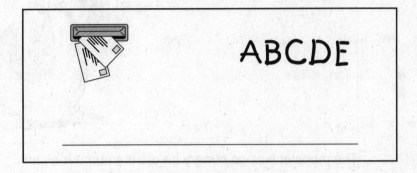

_____

10. Write the word that goes with both pictures on the line.

_____

TIP 4: Some words sound the same. But they mean different things.

Some words sound the same. But they mean different things. They have different spellings, too. Think about the words *ate* and *eight*. Both words sound the same. The word *ate* means something was eaten. The word *eight* is a number.

The monster was so hungry he ate the number eight!

11. Look at the words on the left. Then, match each word with the word it sounds like on the right. The first one has been done for you.

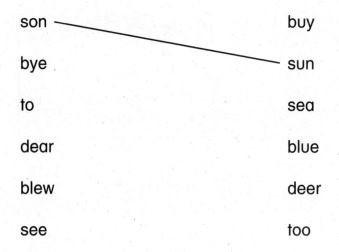

son	buy
bye	sun
to	sea
dear	blue
blew	deer
see	too

TIP 5: Some words look the same. But they have a different sound and meaning.

Some words look the same but sound different. They also mean different things.

Think about the word *live*. You can see a live monkey at the zoo. You can also say you live across the street. The word *live* sounds different in each sentence.

You can say the word *wind* two ways and it means two different things. Look at these two sentences:

In the winter, the wind is very cold.

To get Joe's toy monkey to talk, you need to wind it.

Reading Practice

1. Which word means the opposite of *before*?

   Ⓐ after

   Ⓑ below

   Ⓒ under

2. Read both sentences. Which word fits in both sentences?

   Jennifer put the gold _____ on her finger.

   Can you hear the bells _____?

   Ⓐ talk

   Ⓑ glove

   Ⓒ ring

3. Which word means to "read again"?

   Ⓐ preread

   Ⓑ reread

   Ⓒ misread

4. Which word means the same thing as the word *stairs*?

   Ⓐ floor

   Ⓑ steps

   Ⓒ pairs

5. Which word means "most warm"?

   Ⓐ warmest

   Ⓑ warmer

   Ⓒ warmly

6. Which word means to "bake too much"?

   Ⓐ unbake

   Ⓑ prebake

   Ⓒ overbake

7. Which word sounds like *threw* but means something different?

   Ⓐ through

   Ⓑ three

   Ⓒ thought

Lesson 6: Learning New Words

Do you ever come across words you don't know? When you run into a new word, you can find out what it means by reading the other words and sentences around it. This lesson will help you do that.

Read this story about a poor donkey who is never happy.

The Unhappy Donkey

a fable by Aesop
retold by Alan Noble

One snowy day, a donkey rested in a warm barn. He had a clean bed of straw and good hay to eat. But he was not happy.

"If only it were spring," he said. "Then I could eat the green grass in the fields."

Before long, spring came. The donkey played in the fields and ate lots of green grass. But sometimes the farmer would ask him to pull a small cart to help with the spring planting.

After a while, the donkey said, "I wish it were summer. Then the spring planting would be done, and I could lie in the sun all day."

Before long, summer came. The donkey lay in the tall grass. But sometimes the farmer would ask him to pull a small cart to carry hay from the grassy meadow to the barn.

"I do not like working in the summer," the donkey cried. "It is too hot. I wish it were fall. Then the air would be cool, and I could play in the leaves."

Before long, fall came. The donkey played in the leaves. But sometimes the farmer would ask him to pull a small cart. The donkey had to help carry turnips and other vegetables from the garden to the farmer's house.

"I do not like working in the fall," the donkey cried. "I wish winter would come. I wish I could rest in my warm barn."

Before long, winter came again. Once again the donkey could rest in his warm barn and eat the hay from the meadow.

Do you think the donkey was happy?

TIP 1: The name of a story and the pictures can tell you a lot.

Look at the story's name. It can tell you what the story is about. Also, look at the pictures. They may also help you find out more about the story.

1. What does the name of the story tell you about the donkey?

   _____

2. What does the picture tell you about the donkey?

   _____

 TIP 2: When you see a new word, the rest of the sentence can help you.

Sometimes when you read, you see words you don't know. These words may look strange to you. Don't give up! Read the rest of the sentence. You will know some of the other words in that sentence. They may help you find out what the new word means.

Read this sentence:

> The donkey had to help carry <u>turnips</u> and other vegetables from the garden to the farmer's house.

Do you know what turnips are? (If you do, pretend for a minute that you do not.) The other words in the sentence are signs that will help you.

The sentence says "turnips and other vegetables." The words "and other" tell us that turnips are vegetables.

3. Which other words help show that turnips are vegetables?

   A. The donkey had to help carry

   B. from the garden

   C. to the farmer's house

The words "from the garden" are another sign. Vegetables grow in gardens.

4. Read the sentence that follows. Draw a line under each sign that helps tell you the meaning of the word *meadow*.

> But sometimes the farmer would ask him to pull a small cart to carry hay from the grassy <u>meadow</u> to the barn.

5. What does the word *meadow* mean?

    A. river

    B. house

    C. field

6. Read the sentence. Then circle the correct word.

> "Oh, my!" the donkey (would / wood) say.

Write a sentence using the word you did not circle.

_____

_____

_____

 TIP 3: Write new words in the Word Power Log.

When you find out what a new word means, write it down. Writing down new words can help you remember them. You can write new words in the Word Power Log in this book. The Word Power Log begins on page 168.

What new words did you learn in this lesson?

_____

_____

_____

Reading Practice

Directions: Read the story. Then answer Numbers 1 through 5.

A Day at Wacky World

by Leo Minster

Manny's parents took him to Wacky World for his birthday. Wacky World is a park with rides and games. Manny rode a rollercoaster called The Snake. It had slick steel tracks. Manny felt as if the ride were so fast it could fly him into the sky. At the top, Manny held out his hand to touch the clouds.

Later, Manny's dad won a purple basketball. They ate jumbo hot dogs. At the end of the day, Manny's eyes were heavy. His dad carried him. Manny fell asleep before they made it to the car.

In his dream, Manny saw a man selling gold balloons.

"Can I have one?" Manny asked. His mom gave him money.

"You can have it for free," the man said when Manny offered him money. He picked a balloon the size of the setting sun. "All you got to do is tell Princess Lim that everyone is in place."

"What?" Manny asked, taking the balloon. The man smiled. His teeth were shiny as steel tracks.

Suddenly, Manny felt his feet leave the ground. The balloon was carrying him to the clouds! The clouds became castles. Their walls were as soft as marshmallows. The balloon carried Manny through a window of one of the castles. Inside was a princess. She was wearing a crown on her head. It was shaped like a hot dog.

"Who are you?" Manny asked.

The woman reached into her pocket. She pulled out a silver snake. The snake smiled at Manny and bit his balloon. POP! Manny fell to the soft floor.

"I'm Princess Lim," she smiled. Her eyes were the color of purple basketballs. "And it looks like you're stuck here for a little while."

1. Which word has the same *i*-sound as the word *rides*?

   Ⓐ games

   Ⓑ birthday

   Ⓒ hides

2. Read the sentence from the story.

   Manny felt as if the ride were so <u>fast</u> it could fly him into the sky.

   Which word means the same thing as *fast*?

   Ⓐ slow

   Ⓑ quick

   Ⓒ shiny

3. Which word is made from two words put together?

   Ⓐ balloons

   Ⓑ heavy

   Ⓒ basketball

4. Read this sentence from the story.

   "You can have it for free," the man said when Manny <u>offered</u> him money.

   What does the word *offered* mean?

   Ⓐ tried to give

   Ⓑ took

   Ⓒ talked about

5. Read these sentences from the story.

> Inside was a princess. She was wearing a <u>crown</u> on her head. It was shaped like a hot dog.

What is a crown?

Ⓐ a kind of dress

Ⓑ a kind of hat

Ⓒ a kind of shoe

Lesson 7: Story Signs

When you see a new word, other sentences can help you find out what it means. There are also special books that can tell you what a word means. This lesson will tell you all about these things.

 TIP 1: Other sentences can help show you what a word means.

Sometimes, one sentence may not say enough to tell you what a new word means. Other sentences might have signs that tell you what a word means. Look for signs in other sentences in a paragraph.

A **paragraph** is a group of sentences. Writers group sentences into paragraphs. When you see a new word, you might need to look for signs in the whole paragraph.

Look back at "The Unhappy Donkey," on page 46. It has nine paragraphs.

1. What is the first word in the fourth paragraph?

_____

The next paragraph tells about a make-believe thing called a "tiffle."

> That was the first time I ever saw a fresh <u>tiffle</u>. It was larger than an apple, round, and the color of a banana. I peeled its skin just as I would peel an orange. And here's the really strange part: It tasted like a grapefruit!

2. Read the paragraph again. Draw a line under any signs that help you know what a tiffle is.

3. What is a tiffle?

   A. a kind of fruit

   B. a kind of flower

   C. a kind of candy

Now try doing the same thing with someone in your class. Your teacher will tell you who to work with.

Write a paragraph about a kind of food. Don't say what the food is.

_____

_____

_____

_____

_____

_____

Now show your paragraph to the person you are working with. Can that person guess what the food is? Can you guess what food the other person wrote about?

TIP 2: Other paragraphs can help show you what a word means.

Sometimes, you must read a few paragraphs to find out what a new word means.

Read the next two paragraphs. Then draw a line under any words that help you know what the word *cancel* means.

> It's the first day of vacation, and I have to watch Mrs. Garcia's dog for two weeks! Now I'll have to <u>cancel</u> all the plans I made with Morris for our camping trip.
> "Hello, Morris? I can't go camping with you and your father next weekend. I'm taking care of a neighbor's dog."

Think about these things: The boy has to "cancel all the plans" because he has to watch a neighbor's dog. The next thing he does is call Morris. He tells Morris, "I can't go camping with you and your father next weekend."

4. What does the word *cancel* mean?

    A. walk the dog

    B. call off

    C. plan for

Write your answer from Number 4 in this sentence. Does it work?

The boy had to _____ his plan to go

camping with a friend.

TIP 3: A dictionary can tell you what a word means.

What do you do if you still can't figure out a new word? You open a dictionary. A **dictionary** is a book that tells you what words mean.

A dictionary can give you lots of other information, too. It can show you the syllables in a word. You learned about syllables in Lesson 1. A dictionary uses dots to show you the different syllables.

In a dictionary, words starting with the letter *a* come first. Words starting with the letter *z* come last. Look at this example:

---

foot – forever   31

---

foot, *noun* a part of the body used for walking

fore•head, *noun* the part of the face above the eyes

for•est, *noun* a large group of trees

for•ev•er, *adverb* at all times; always

---

5. How many syllables are there in the word *forever*?

   A. one

   B. two

   C. three

TIP 4: A glossary can tell you what a word means.

Some books have a glossary. A **glossary** is a list of words and what they mean. You can find a glossary at the ends of some books. The glossary is like a dictionary because it tells you what a word means. A dictionary has lots of words. A glossary has words that are in the book you are reading. Look at this example:

> **Glossary**
>
> **ice age**   a time long ago when much
>   of the earth was covered by ice
>
> **insect**   a small animal that has six legs
>   and a body made of three parts
>
> **larva**   the young form of an insect
>
> **lava**   melted rock that comes up onto
>   the top of the earth

6. What does the word *lava* mean?

   A. melted rock

   B. a small animal

   C. a long period of time

TIP 5: A thesaurus can help you find other words that mean the same thing.

In Lesson 5, you learned about words that are the same and different. These words are called synonyms and antonyms. A **thesaurus** is a book that gives you lists of synonyms. It can also give you a list of antonyms for a word. Look at this example:

	Page 73
knock	(*verb*) pound, hit, rap, tap
	L
lady	(*noun*) woman
large	(*adj.*) big, huge **antonym:** small
laugh	(*noun* or *verb*) chuckle, giggle
loud	(*adj.*) noisy **antonym:** quiet

TIP 6: Make sure you know your ABCs.

Knowing your ABCs can help you find words in dictionaries and other word lists. Dictionaries and other word lists are in alphabetical order. *Order* means what comes first, second, third, and so on. **Alphabetical order** means words come in the same order as the alphabet.

Write in the missing letters in the alphabet.

A __ C D __ __ __ H I __ K L __

N O P Q __ __ __ U V W X __ Z

7. Look at the first letter of these words. Write the words in alphabetical order.

boy   fox   girl   apple   zoom

_____

_____

_____

_____

The dictionary starts by listing all the words that begin with the letter *a*. Then you need to look at the second letter. The words that start with *ab* come before the words that start with *ac*. Look at this list of words from the beginning pages of a dictionary.

about

across

add

afraid

The word *about* is listed before the word *across* even though both words begin with an *a*. Why? Because of the second letter in each word. The letter *b* in *about* comes before the letter *c* in *across*.

8. All of these words begin with the letter *b*. Look at the second letter of each word. Then, list the words in alphabetical order.

    book   back   bean   big   bug

_____

_____

_____

_____

9. Jason and Melissa have found the names of six kinds of fish in a library book. Help them put the names of those fish in alphabetical order.

    bass   goldfish   bluefish   trout   catfish   sunfish

_____

_____

_____

_____

_____

_____

Reading Practice

Directions: Read the story. Then answer Numbers 1 through 6.

Strange Pets

by Julianna Weich

Some boys and girls have dogs or cats for pets. Others have fish or birds. Still others have very different animals for pets.

My friend Bobby has a pet named Lulu. Lulu looks a little like a camel. But she doesn't have a hump on her back like camels do. Bobby rides on Lulu sometimes. Lulu's ancestors came from the Andes Mountains of South America. But Lulu and her parents were born in the United States. Can you guess what kind of pet Lulu is?

People can't believe their eyes when they see Justin walking his pet. Wilbur weighs more than Justin does! Wilbur walks slowly. He uses a snout to smell with. Wilbur has a curly tail. Do you know what kind of animal Wilbur is?

Miss Muffet is hairy and brown. She looks very scary, but Jeremy likes her a lot. Miss Muffet is smaller than Jeremy's hand. She has eight strong legs and can crawl very fast. She sheds her old skin two times a year. She moves out of her old skin and leaves it behind. Then it looks as if there are two Miss Muffets in the cage. Do you know what kind of pet Miss Muffet is?

My pet Speedy looks like a tiny dinosaur. She lives in a glass bowl with sand and stones in it. Sometimes she hides under the rocks. Other times, she lies on top of the rocks to enjoy the sunshine. Speedy eats lots of insects, like flies and crickets. Speedy can move very fast. Can you guess what Speedy is?

1. Read these sentences from "Strange Pets."

   Lulu looks a little like a small camel. But she doesn't have a <u>hump</u> on her back like camels do.

   What does the word *hump* mean?

   Ⓐ bump

   Ⓑ bag

   Ⓒ seat

2. Read these sentences from "Strange Pets."

   Lulu's <u>ancestors</u> came from the Andes Mountains of South America. But Lulu and her parents were born in the United States.

   What does the word *ancestors* mean?

   Ⓐ friends

   Ⓑ grandparents

   Ⓒ owners

3. Read this sentence from "Strange Pets."

   He uses a <u>snout</u> to smell with.

   What does the word *snout* mean?

   Ⓐ tail

   Ⓑ foot

   Ⓒ nose

4. Read these sentences from "Strange Pets."

   She <u>sheds</u> her old skin two times a year. She moves out of her old skin and leaves it behind.

   What does the word *sheds* mean?

   Ⓐ wears

   Ⓑ grows

   Ⓒ comes out of

5. Read this sentence from "Strange Pets."

   Speedy eats lots of <u>insects</u>, such as flies and crickets.

   What does the word *insects* mean?

   Ⓐ bugs

   Ⓑ seeds

   Ⓒ worms

6. Draw a line to connect the pet's name with its picture.

   Miss Muffet   Speedy   Lulu   Wilbur

Unit 2

Understanding What You Read

Have you ever missed the first part of a TV show? When you came into the room, what did you ask everyone there? You probably said something like, "What's it about?" Once you know a little more about a show, it is more fun to watch.

Asking questions is important with stories, too. In this unit, you'll learn more about asking questions when you read. You'll learn lots of ways to find out more about what you are reading. And, you'll learn about looking at pictures, maps, and directions.

In This Unit

The Big Picture

Important Details

Asking Questions

Making
   Connections

Writer's Purpose

All About Books

Reading Pictures

Maps and
   Directions

Lesson 8: The Big Picture

Telling someone about the big picture means telling someone what something is about. When you tell someone what something is about, you tell them the big things. Who is in the story? Is it scary? Is it happy? Is it funny? Do the people learn something? All of these things help tell about the big picture.

Before you read this story, look at the picture below. Then read the story name. What do you think this story will be about?

_____

_____

_____

Great Friends

by Linda Austin

Mrs. Corelli lived next door to Emily. She was older than Emily's grandmother. Emily thought her neighbor was very nice.

In the summer, Emily would go outside to play after breakfast. She would pick up Mrs. Corelli's newspaper and take it to the lady's door. Mrs. Corelli thought Emily was the most wonderful little girl.

Mrs. Corelli sometimes baked cookies just for Emily. The cookies were big, round, and filled with chocolate chips. Emily liked to sit on the porch swing with Mrs. Corelli and eat the cookies. They talked about all sorts of things.

Other times, Emily's friend Lisa joined them. Mrs. Corelli taught the girls how to play games she had learned when she was young.

For many years, Emily and Mrs. Corelli were great friends. As Emily grew up, she made many other friends, too. But she never forgot about her neighbor. Emily had learned from Mrs. Corelli that great friends do not have to be the same age.

Did you correctly guess what the story was about?

 TIP 1: Find out what the story is about.

Every kind of writing has a main idea. The **main idea** tells what the story is mostly about.

Stories can have many important ideas. But there is only one *most* important idea. That most important idea is the main idea. Your job as a reader is to find out what the main idea is.

Here are some of the important ideas in the story you just read:

- Emily picks up the newspaper for Mrs. Corelli.
- Mrs. Corelli bakes cookies for Emily.

1. What is one more important idea about Emily and Mrs. Corelli?

_____

_____

_____

2. What is the main idea in the story about Emily and Mrs. Corelli?

A. They sit on the porch.

B. They are great friends.

C. They eat cookies.

TIP 2: A paragraph can have a main idea.

Each paragraph in a story has a main idea, too. Think about what each paragraph is about.

Read the second paragraph of "Great Friends" again.

3. What is the main idea in the second paragraph?

   A. Emily goes outside after breakfast in the summer.

   B. Emily picks up Mrs. Corelli's newspaper.

   C. Mrs. Corelli thinks Emily is a wonderful girl.

 TIP 3: Look for the main idea sentence.

Sometimes a writer will put the main idea in one sentence. In the next paragraph, one sentence tells the main idea. All the other sentences tell about that main idea.

> Heather ate two eggs. She ate two pieces of toast. She ate a bowl of cereal. She drank a small glass of orange juice. Then she drank a cup of hot chocolate. Heather liked to eat a big breakfast.

4. Which sentence tells the most important idea of the paragraph?

   A. Heather ate two eggs.

   B. She drank a small glass of orange juice.

   C. Heather liked to eat a big breakfast.

5. In the space below, draw a picture of Heather's breakfast.

TIP 4: Say the main idea in your own words.

Sometimes writers don't tell the main idea in a sentence. They let you find the main idea on your own. Then you need to say the main idea in your own words.

Read the paragraph. It was written by a girl named Jane.

> My mom used to have time to spend with me. Now Mom is too tired to play with me. No one plays with me anymore. They all play with my new brother, Davy. They "ooh" and "aah" at every move he makes. They act like they've never seen a baby before.

The writer does not tell the main idea in the paragraph. Instead, she says a lot of other things that tell you what the main idea is. She wants you to find out the main idea on your own.

6. What do you think this story is mostly about?

_____

_____

_____

_____

Think about your answer to Number 6 as you read the next question.

7. What is the main idea of the paragraph?

    A. Jane has a new little brother whose name is Davy.

    B. Jane doesn't like the changes since Davy was born.

    C. Jane's mom seems to be more tired than she used to be.

 TIP 5: Details tell about the main idea.

The walls of a house hold up the roof. We say these walls support the roof. To **support** something means to hold it up.

In a story, details support the main idea. A **detail** is part of a story or paragraph that tells what things look like. Details also tell what things sound like, what they taste like, and what they feel like. They can even tell you what things smell like! They tell who the people or animals in the story are. They can also tell what these people or animals are thinking. All stories have details.

Do you remember the story of Jane? Jane says that her brother's name is Davy. This is not the main idea of the paragraph. But it is a detail.

8. Read Jane's paragraph on page 68 again. Find two details that tell about the main idea. Write them on lines A and B.

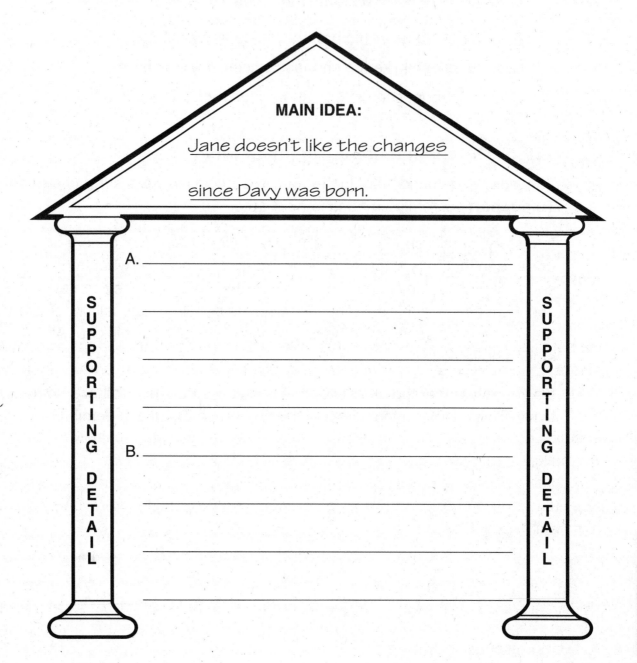

MAIN IDEA:

Jane doesn't like the changes

since Davy was born.

A. _____

_____

_____

_____

B. _____

_____

_____

SUPPORTING DETAIL

SUPPORTING DETAIL

Reading Practice

Directions: Read the story. Then answer Numbers 1 through 5.

Sam and Kai

by Susan McCarty

Our school is small. When the new student showed up, everyone knew about him right away. His name was Kai, and he was from a place far away called Japan. When he talked, his words sounded different than ours. Some of the kids thought the way he talked sounded strange. They made fun of him. At lunch, no one sat with Kai. He looked sad, so I sat with him.

"Hi Kai," I said. "My name is Sam. How do you like our school so far?"

"I like it. It's smaller than my school in Japan. That is nice because it's easy to remember everyone's name."

I nodded, "That's true."

We talked for a while. Even though we were from different parts of the world, we both liked many of the same things. We both loved baseball. We talked about different teams in America and Japan. Kai said the best baseball team in Japan is the Seibu Lions. Then the bell rang.

"Thank you for sitting with me, Sam," said Kai. "You should come to a baseball game with me and my family. My dad loves American baseball. When we moved here, he got season tickets to see the Colorado Rockies."

"I'd love to go to a game with you. Thanks Kai!" I said. I was glad I sat with Kai. He was nice and funny. Also, he knew a lot about baseball. We would have a great time together!

1. What is the main idea of the first paragraph?

Ⓐ The school is small.

Ⓑ Kai is new at school.

Ⓒ Japan is a place far away.

2. What do Sam and Kai both like?

   Ⓐ baseball

   Ⓑ basketball

   Ⓒ swimming

3. Read the sentence from "Sam and Kai."

   Kai said the <u>best</u> team in Japan is the Seibu Lions.

   What word means the same as the word *best*?

   Ⓐ saddest

   Ⓑ funny

   Ⓒ greatest

4. What does Kai ask Sam to do?

   Ⓐ tell him everyone's name

   Ⓑ sit with him at lunch

   Ⓒ go to a baseball game

5. What is the main idea of "Sam and Kai"?

   Ⓐ Sam and Kai eat lunch together.

   Ⓑ Sam and Kai become friends.

   Ⓒ Sam and Kai both love baseball.

Lesson 9: Important Details

Do you know the story "Goldilocks and the Three Bears"? Could you retell the story if someone asked you to? Do you remember what Goldilocks did? Whose bed did Goldilocks fall asleep in?

You can answer all of these questions by looking at a story's details. In Lesson 8, you learned that details are important because they tell about what things look like, sound like, and so on. Details help explain the main idea of the story. They also make the story more fun to read.

This lesson will teach you many things about the details that support the main idea.

Two Charlies

by Juanita Kopaska

Charlie did not do very well in school. He was not good at sports. He was shy and afraid of girls.

But Charlie was good at one thing in school. He could draw pictures called cartoons. He was very proud of his drawings.

Charlie began selling some of his cartoons when he was about 25 years old.

When he was 28, Charlie began drawing a cartoon boy. This boy was a lot like Charlie himself. The cartoon boy did not do well in school. He was not very good at sports. He was shy. He was afraid of girls. And his name was Charlie, too.

The cartoon boy was Charlie Brown. There were other cartoon boys and girls, too. The story of these cartoon boys and girls was called *Peanuts*. Every week, there was a little cartoon story about Charlie Brown and his friends in the newspaper.

The man who drew Charlie Brown for over 50 years was Charles M. Schulz. "Charlie" is a nickname for "Charles." Mr. Schulz also created Lucy, Linus, Snoopy, and the rest of the *Peanuts* cartoon boys and girls.

Peanuts was read by people all over. It helped the two shy Charlies become known and loved around the world.

Charles Schulz

Every story has a main idea. In "Two Charlies," the main idea is that the two Charlies were the same in many ways. We know that Charles Schulz and Charlie Brown were like each other because the story's details tell us so.

TIP 1: Details help you understand the main idea.

Details are the little pieces of information in a story. They help us understand the main idea. They help us answer questions about the main idea, too. In the story "Two Charlies," the details show how Charles Schulz and Charlie Brown were like each other.

1. When Charles Schulz was in school, what was he proud of?

   A. playing sports

   B. drawing cartoons

   C. being a good student

2. Who is Charlie Brown?

   A. a boy in a cartoon

   B. a boy who likes cartoons

   C. Charles Schulz's friend

3. What is the name of the cartoon stories Charles Schulz drew?

   A. *Snoopy*

   B. *Peanuts*

   C. *Charlie Brown*

TIP 2: A main idea web can help you remember a story.

A **main idea web** is a picture that shows you the main idea and details of a story. You can draw one to help you remember a story.

Here's a main idea web for "Two Charlies."

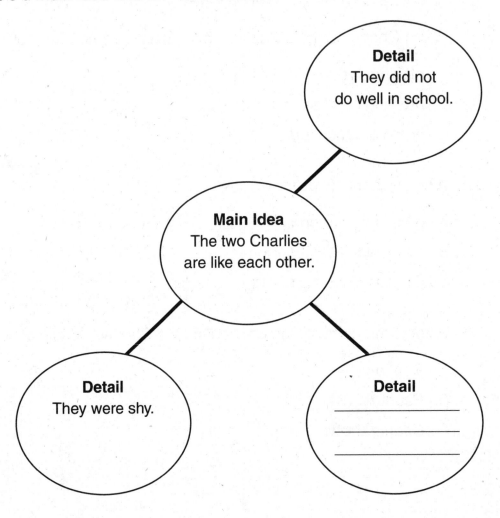

4. Which detail can be added to the main idea web?

    A. They both drew cartoons.

    B. They were both proud.

    C. They were not good at sports.

TIP 3: Details make pictures with words.

Details help you see the story in your mind.

Here is a sentence without many details:

> I like being in this room.

What room is the sentence talking about? We just don't know. The sentence doesn't tell us. We need details to know more.

Here is a paragraph full of details about that room.

> I like being in this room. The room has **a bed** and **a desk**. It also has **a clock**, **a telephone**, and **a television**.

Now we know more. We know what's in the room. We can begin to see it on our own.

Here's another paragraph that uses even more details. Use these details to help you draw a picture in your mind.

> I like being in this **large room**. The room has a **soft** bed and a desk **with five drawers**. It also has a **yellow** clock, a **green** telephone, and a **big** television.

5. Now draw a picture of the room. Use crayons or colored pencils to show details from the paragraph.

Reading Practice

Directions: Read the story. Then answer Numbers 1 through 5.

That's Never Going to Happen!
by Glenda Goodwyn

Abe's family was always moving. Abe never had time to make friends or go to school. Abe wished his family could stay in one place.

"Sorry, son," his father said. "We must go where the land is good."

Farming was all Abe knew. His only friends were the vegetables in the ground. His only school was the farm. The only thing he ever learned about was farming.

By the time Abe was older, he had moved from Kentucky to Indiana to Illinois. In Illinois, Abe hoped that he could start school. But Abe's father needed help on the farm. Then something terrible happened. Abe's mother got very sick and died. Abe's father decided to move again. This time, Abe said no. He wanted to learn something other than farming. He wanted so badly to read.

"Abe the reader?" people laughed. "That's never going to happen!"

Abe didn't listen. He knew he could do it. He met people who carried books. Abe started listening to people read. He learned the sounds of letters. One day, Abe walked 20 miles just to borrow a book!

Soon, Abe learned how to read. He had never gone to school and he was reading whole books! He wanted to change things so that children could go to school and learn.

One day, Abe said he wanted to run for president.

"Abe Lincoln the President?" people laughed. "That's never going to happen!"

Abe smiled. He knew he could do it. And after all, he had been laughed at before.

1. What did Abe spend most of his time doing when he was little?

   Ⓐ working on the farm

   Ⓑ reading books

   Ⓒ listening to people read

2. Why does Abe feel like his only friends are vegetables?

   Ⓐ He only has time for farming.

   Ⓑ Abe loves farming very much.

   Ⓒ Everyone laughs at him.

3. How many syllables does the word *terrible* have?

   Ⓐ two

   Ⓑ three

   Ⓒ four

4. Why do people laugh at Abe?

   Ⓐ They think he is a funny person.

   Ⓑ They don't think he can do what he wants.

   Ⓒ Abe has vegetables as friends.

5. What is the main idea of the story?

   Ⓐ Abe learned a lot about farming.

   Ⓑ Abe wanted to learn how to read.

   Ⓒ Abe knew he could do anything.

Lesson 10: Asking Questions

Do you ask questions when you read? It's a really good thing to do. There are lots of questions you can ask when you read. Questions can help you find important ideas and details in what you read. In this lesson, you will learn about some important questions you can ask.

 TIP 1: Asking questions helps you find the details.

A reporter is a person who writes stories in newspapers. Before a reporter writes a story, she asks a lot of questions. The answers to these questions are the details. She'll put them in her story.

The Reporter's Questions

Who?

What?

When?

Where?

Why?

How?

You can ask these questions about true stories and about made-up stories. As you read, ask yourself these reporter's questions. Then look for the details that answer those questions.

TIP 2: Ask yourself "What if?" questions.

You can also ask yourself "What if?" questions. These questions will help you understand the things you read about. Here are three examples:

What if the little girl meets a wolf in the woods?

What if Joe moves to another city?

What if Wendy doesn't know how to swim?

Read the following newspaper story.

Circus will open in Gotham City on Friday

Ben Post is the ringmaster of the Bellwater Circus. He said today that the circus will open in Gotham City on Friday afternoon as planned.

Many people were afraid that the circus would not open until later next week. The show's lions and elephants went to Metropolis by mistake. Post said this happened because of a trucking mix-up.

"Our trucks are bringing the animals back to Gotham City right now," Post said. "Hang on to your tickets. The show will open on time."

Now write some questions that can be answered by the details in the story. We did the first question for you.

1. Write a "who?" question about the story.

<u>Who is the ringmaster of the Gotham City Circus?</u>

_____

2. Write a "why?" question about the story.

_____

_____

3. Write a "what if?" question about the story.

_____

_____

4. Write a "where?" question about the story.

_____

_____

5. Which of these "how?" questions is answered by the newspaper story?

   A. How did Ben Post get the job of ringmaster?

   B. How many people have tickets for the circus?

   C. How are the animals being moved to Gotham City?

6. Circle the drawing that best tells about the main idea of the newspaper story.

A.

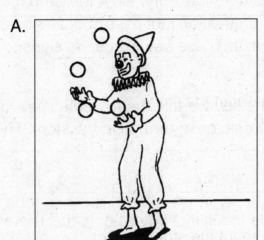

B.

C.

TIP 3: Key words are signs that help you find the answers.

Key words are important words from the story. On a test, you must answer questions. Sometimes, a question that asks about details will have important words from the story in it. These key words are signs to help you find the answer to the question.

Most questions have at least one key word in them. Sometimes the answers also have key words. Look for key words in the story. They will help you find the correct answer.

Read the passage below:

> There were many people to tell that boy what to do. There was his mother and his father, his grandfather, and his older brother. And there was also an aunt, who was always saying: "Do this. Do that." Every day this aunt would shout at him and make a great noise that would frighten the birds.
> The boy did not like his aunt.

> —from "Strange Animals," *Children of Wax: African Folk Tales*
> by Alexander McCall Smith

Read the questions that follow. They are about the passage you just read. Some key words are printed in dark letters. Look for these key words in the passage. They will help you find the answers.

7. Who **tells** the boy **what to do**?

   A. many people

   B. only his aunt

   C. only his mother

8. Which word best tells about the boy's **brother**?

   A. bigger

   B. older

   C. stronger

9. What does the boy's **aunt** do that would **frighten the birds**?

   A. She throws things.

   B. She runs after the boy.

   C. She makes a great noise.

 TIP 4: Think about what happens first.

Details help us put events in order. Sometimes detail questions will ask what happened first, next, or last.

Read the story below. As you read, picture the story in your mind. Picture what happens to Ely and his dog, Banjo. This will help you remember what happens first, next, and last in the story.

Flying Kites
by Pauline Stark

Ely decided to take his dog, Banjo, to the park on Saturday. The sun was shining. The sky was blue. It was a beautiful day for a walk in the park.

When they got to the park, Ely saw six different kites in the sky. They were all different shapes and colors. A bunch of different kids and adults were flying them.

One kite had a bright red ladybug on it. Another kite looked like a green dragon. There was one kite that was all different colors and looked like an empty box.

Ely was watching the kites when he felt the leash jerk out of his hand. Banjo was running away! Ely chased after him into the bushes. He found Banjo with a small kite in his jaws. "Where did you get that, boy?" Ely asked Banjo. A little girl came up to them.

"It's my kite. I was running to get it, and your dog chased me."

"I'm sorry," said Ely. "But he's a really friendly dog. He just thought you were playing." Ely patted Banjo on the head and the girl did the same.

On page 171, you will see four boxes. Inside each box is a picture. These pictures tell about the story you have just read. Carefully cut out the boxes and lay them on your desk.

Now we will use the pictures to retell the story.

10. Put the pictures in the same order as the story. Put the picture of the first thing that happens in Box 1. Then, put the picture of the second thing that happens in Box 2, and so on.

When your pictures are in the right order, glue them in the boxes on page 87.

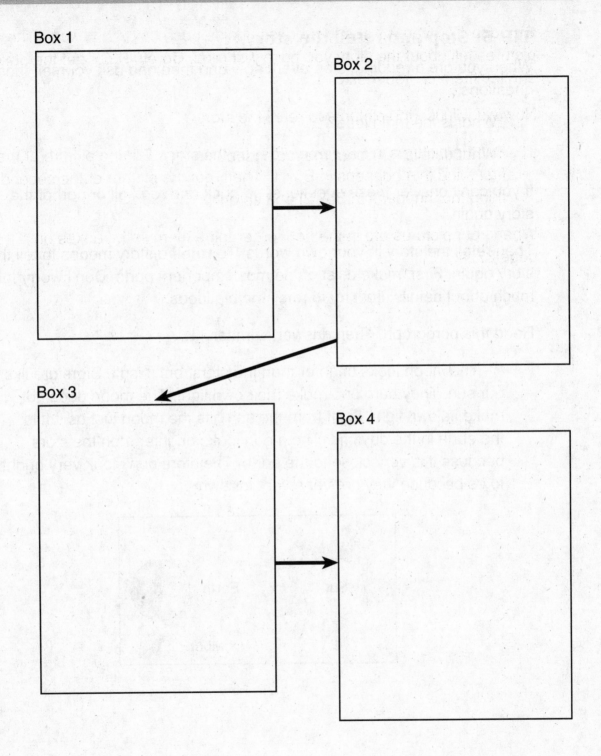

Box 1

Box 2

Box 3

Box 4

TIP 5: Stop and retell the story.

When you are a reading, stop every now and then and ask yourself these questions:

"What is the main idea?"

"What details tell about the main idea?"

If you can't answer these questions, go back and read all or part of the story again.

Then retell the story in your own words. To **retell** a story means to tell the story again. First, make a list of the most important parts. Don't worry too much about details. Just try to retell the big ideas.

Read this paragraph. Then answer Number 11.

> The moon looks brighter than the stars, but it isn't. Stars are like our sun. They burn and make their own light. The moon does not make its own light. Light from the sun hits the moon just as it hits the earth in the daytime. The moon looks brighter than the stars because it is very close to the earth. The stars don't look very bright to us because they are very, very far away.

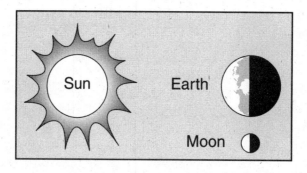

11. List two important parts of the paragraph.

_____

_____

_____

_____

_____

_____

Reading Practice

Directions: Read the story. Then answer Numbers 1 through 6.

Lori's Surprise
by Barbara L. Hauth

Amy called Lori to come over and play. Lori put on her skates. She skated down the sidewalk to Amy's house. At Amy's house, Lori found a note. Here is what it said:

```
        If you are Lori, go
        to Carlos's house.
                Love,
                    Amy
```

Lori skated to Carlos's house. She rang the doorbell. Carlos's mother answered the door. "Hi, Lori," she said. "Carlos asked me to tell you to go to David's house."

At David's house, Lori saw a note on the mailbox. This is what it said:

```
    Lori,
    Go to the big tree
    by Justin's house. Be
    as quiet as a mouse.
```

Lori skated to Justin's house. She leaned against the big, old oak tree and listened.

Justin's voice said over and over, "Lori, please go to Keesha's house. Lori, please go to Keesha's house. Lori, please go to Keesha's house." The voice came from a small tape recorder in the hollow of the tree.

Lori skated up to Keesha's front door.

"Oh, good," Lori said. "This time there's no note." Keesha's mother opened the door. She asked Lori to come in.

Soon, balloons, horns, and five faces appeared around the corner. "Surprise! Happy birthday, Lori!" All of Lori's friends were there.

Lori was very surprised. "My birthday isn't until next week!"

"We know," said Keesha. "We wanted to surprise you. So we're having your party today."

Lori smiled a great big smile. It was fun to have such wonderful friends.

1. What happens first in the story?

   Ⓐ Lori leans on a big, old oak tree.

   Ⓑ Amy calls Lori to come over and play.

   Ⓒ Keesha's mother opens the front door.

2. How does Lori go from house to house?

   Ⓐ on a bicycle

   Ⓑ on a skateboard

   Ⓒ on skates

3. What does Lori find at Justin's house?

   Ⓐ a note on the mailbox

   Ⓑ a tape recorder with a message

   Ⓒ balloons, horns, and her friends

4. Where does Lori finally get her surprise?

   Ⓐ at David's house

   Ⓑ at Lori's house

   Ⓒ at Keesha's house

5. Look at this drawing.

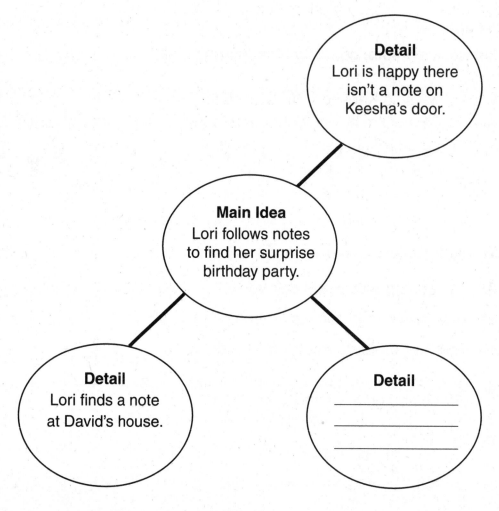

What sentence goes on the blank lines?

Ⓐ Lori skates to Justin's house and leans against a tree.

Ⓑ Keesha likes to write notes for Lori to find.

Ⓒ Lori uses skates because her bicycle is broken.

6. Which of these words is in the same word family as the word *house*?

Ⓐ skates

Ⓑ horns

Ⓒ mouse

Lesson 11: Making Connections

In made-up stories, there is always some kind of big problem. There may be many smaller problems, too.

Sometimes, the writer tells you exactly what the main problem is. Most of the time, you have to find out the main problem by yourself. You do this by putting together details.

Read the following story.

Mouse Trouble

by Rafael Rogers

It was a morning like any other morning. Julie sat at the table eating her breakfast. Her mom was getting ready for work.

Julie sat at the table. She looked out the door of the kitchen. Their back door was all glass. She watched the birds flying around. Then she saw her cat, Tabby, at the door.

Julie got up and let him in without looking at him. Just as Julie was closing the door, her mom walked into the kitchen.

"Julie!" she said. "Why did you let Tabby in the house? He has a mouse!" Julie's mom tried to grab Tabby. Just as she got near him, Tabby set the mouse on the floor. The mouse ran across the kitchen. Julie jumped and bumped the table. Her cup fell on the floor. Tabby ran right through the milk as he was chasing the mouse.

Tabby ran across Julie's schoolbag, getting it all full of milk. The the mouse ran right over Julie's mom's feet! Her mom screamed! Then it turned around and ran right under Julie! As the mouse ran to the living room, Tabby ran after the mouse. Julie's mom ran after Tabby. Julie didn't know what to do. So she ran after her mom to see what would happen.

The mouse ran into the living room and behind a chair. Tabby was trying to get behind the chair, too. Julie's mom pushed the chair out of the way so they could see where the mouse was. But the mouse was gone. Tabby kept poking his paw at the wall. They moved him out of the way. They saw a tiny hole in the wall. The mouse had found a way out.

Julie's mom let out a deep breath. "Well we better start cleaning up this mess," she said. Julie looked around. There were milk footprints all over the room. Then she remembered there was still milk all over the kitchen floor. Julie thought her mom was mad, but then she saw her mom smile. Julie went back to the kitchen to start cleaning.

Julie's mom was glad the mouse was gone. So was Julie. But Tabby looked mad. He wanted to play with the mouse some more. But Julie thought the mouse was probably pretty happy after all. Now all Julie had to do was help her mom clean up and get to school on time.

In the story you just read, Julie is eating her breakfast. When she sees Tabby at the door, she lets him in. Julie doesn't look at Tabby to see if he has anything in his mouth. This is the start of the problems. This helps make a bigger problem.

1. Read the story again and draw a line under some of the problems.

2. What is the main problem in the story?

    A. The house is a mess.

    B. Tabby catches a mouse.

    C. Julie has to clean up.

TIP 1: Retelling the story will help you understand it.

The **events** in a story are the things that happen. Retelling a story's events in order will help you understand it.

Events in a story are like the numbers in a dot-to-dot drawing. You have to put your pencil at dot number 1 to draw a line to dot number 2. In a story, the first event (1) has to happen before the second event (2) can happen.

Here's a dot-to-dot picture for you to finish. It will show something from the story "Mouse Trouble."

3. With your pencil, connect the dots in order from 1 to 18.

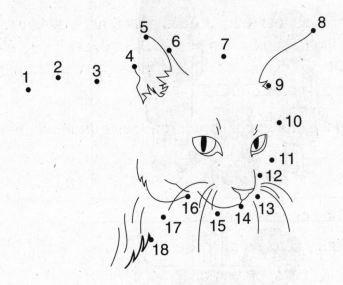

4. Put these story events in order by numbering the boxes from 1 to 4.

_____

_____

_____

_____

5. Think of a story you know well. This story might be "Little Red Riding Hood," "The Three Little Pigs," or another story. Write what happens in the story on the lines below.

_____

_____

_____

_____

_____

_____

_____

_____

_____

TIP 2: One event makes another event happen.

Most of the time, one event in a story causes another event. To **cause** something means to make something happen.

Think about dominos. Steve sets up a row of dominos. He pushes the first domino and it falls. Steve makes the domino fall. He is the cause.

The first domino makes the second domino fall. The first domino causes the second domino to fall.

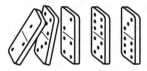

Think back to the story "Mouse Trouble." In that story, there is a reason why the house gets messy.

6. Look back at the story. Draw a line under the sentence or sentences that tell what makes the house messy.

7. Why does Julie's house get messy?

   A. Julie is eating breakfast before school.

   B. The cat wants to come into the house.

   C. Tabby lets a mouse go in the house.

TIP 3: You can put events together by making a "because" sentence.

You can put events together by making a "because" sentence. The word *because* can show how one event causes another.

> Julie lets Tabby in the house *because* she doesn't see that he has a mouse.

> Julie's milk spills *because* Julie bumps into the table.

8. Finish this "because" sentence about the story.

   The mouse runs around the house because

   _____

   _____

   _____

   _____ .

 TIP 4: The solution is how a problem is fixed.

The **solution** is how a problem is fixed. To **solve** a problem means to fix the problem. Sometimes the writer tells you about the solution. Sometimes you have to guess how the problem will be fixed. The story's details will help you.

9. Look back at the story. Draw a box around any sentences that tell you how Julie and her mom will solve the problem of the messy house.

10. How will Julie and her mom solve the problem of the messy house?

   _____

   _____

   _____

   _____

TIP 5: Think about the story and your own life.

Sometimes it helps to ask yourself if the story makes you think of something in your own life. This can help you understand how the people in the story feel.

11. Do the details of the story "Mouse Trouble" make you think of something that has happened in your own life? Write about a time someone or something made a mess.

_____

_____

_____

_____

12. How is your story the same as "Mouse Trouble"?

_____

_____

_____

13. How is your story different from "Mouse Trouble"?

_____

_____

_____

Reading Practice

Directions: Read the story. Then answer Numbers 1 through 6.

The Wrong Bus
Robert Nord

It was the first day of school. Jody stood at the end of his street. He was waiting for the bus. Jody had never taken the bus before. His mom had always taken him to school. But over the summer, his mom got a new job. She had to be at work earlier than before. She couldn't take Jody to school anymore. That was okay with Jody because he thought the bus might be fun. Who would be on it? Would he make new friends on the bus? After a while, he began to worry. Where was the bus? It seemed like he'd been standing outside for a long time.

Finally, a school bus pulled up. His heart beat a little harder as he climbed up the stairs. He got to the top of the stairs and began to walk toward the back. As he walked, he looked at some of the kids on the bus. They looked older than Jody . . . a lot older. Oh no! He must have gotten on the high school bus. He ran back up to the front to tell the driver, but the bus had already pulled away.

"Wait, I'm on the wrong bus!" Jody said to the driver.

"Well, that's a problem," said the driver. "What do you want me to do?"

Jody thought for a moment. He couldn't stay on the bus. What would he do at the high school all day? His mom couldn't come pick him up because she was at work. And he didn't want to miss the first day of school. He looked out the window at the rows of houses as they passed. They looked like little boxes in all different colors. He'd seen those boxes before! He watched out the window a little longer until he found the house he was looking for. It was Jason's house! His mom had driven him here many times. Farther down the street, Jody saw Jason standing at the corner. He was waiting for the bus to the elementary school.

"Let me off here. It's my friend's bus stop! I'll get on the right bus with him."

"Good idea," said the bus driver. "I'm glad you know what to do." He pulled the bus to the side of the road. Jody got off the bus. Boy was he glad to see Jason!

1. What happens first in the story?

   Ⓐ Jody sees Jason's house.

   Ⓑ Jody gets on the wrong bus.

   Ⓒ Jody waits for the bus.

2. What is Jody's main problem?

   Ⓐ Jody is on the high school bus.

   Ⓑ Jody has to go to school.

   Ⓒ Jody's mom gets a new job.

3. Why does Jody take the bus?

   Ⓐ He wants to see what taking the bus is like.

   Ⓑ Jason also takes the bus to school.

   Ⓒ Jody's mom has to be at work earlier.

4. What are the boxes Jody sees from the bus?

   Ⓐ dogs

   Ⓑ houses

   Ⓒ toys

5. Why does Jody tell the driver to let him get off the bus?

   Ⓐ Jody is afraid of the kids on the bus.

   Ⓑ Jody sees his friend waiting for the bus.

   Ⓒ Jody is near where his mom works.

6. How will Jody solve his problem?

   Ⓐ He will take the right bus with Jason.

   Ⓑ He will call his mom from the high school.

   Ⓒ He will not go to school on the first day.

Lesson 12: Writer's Purpose

A **purpose** for something is why we do it. Every writer writes for a purpose. We call that the writer's purpose. It's why the writer wrote something.

 TIP 1: Every writer has a purpose for writing.

Sometimes writers want to teach us something. Sometimes they want to scare us. And sometimes they want us to do something. They might want us to buy a toy or go to a new movie.

1. What other thing might a writer want to make us do?

_____

_____

_____

Passage is another word for story. Read this passage about food for birds. It will help you with the tips in this lesson.

Fast Food for Birds

by Jason Allister

What if birds could eat fast food, just like people do? What kind of food would they order?

What if you opened a restaurant for birds? You would need to put seeds on your menu. Sparrows and other small birds eat small seeds. Bigger birds, like cardinals, eat big seeds. They open the seeds with their beaks. Then they eat the food inside. Birds are messy eaters. They drop parts of seeds on the floor. Too bad you will have to sweep the floor a lot!

This might be gross, but bugs would have to be on the menu, too. Woodpeckers eat bugs. Many birds eat beetles and grasshoppers.

Some very big birds eat lizards and snakes. Owls eat mice, squirrels, rabbits, frogs, and other animals. But there's a problem. Owls hunt in the dark. You don't mind keeping your restaurant open all night, do you?

Robins and other birds eat worms for breakfast. They use sharp beaks to pull worms out of the ground. It looks like a game of tug-of-war! It's fun to watch robins find their breakfast!

Hummingbirds have long beaks. They drink nectar. Nectar is sweet and found in flowers. If hummingbirds come to your restaurant, you could give them sugar water. They like that, too.

Here's a simple way to open a bird restaurant: Wash out an empty milk jug. Cut a hole in it. Tie on a string to hang it from a tree branch. Fill the jug with birdseed. It's as easy as that!

TIP 2: The main idea can help you find the writer's purpose.

In Lesson 8, you learned about the main idea. The **main idea** tells what a passage is mostly about. Learning the main idea of a story will help you understand the writer's purpose. Look for the main idea in the passage you just read.

2. What is the main idea of "Fast Food for Birds"?

    A. Hummingbirds drink their food.

    B. Robins like to eat worms.

    C. Birds eat many different kinds of food.

The writer of "Fast Food for Birds" is trying to teach his readers about the kinds of food birds eat. He also wants them to do something. Look at the end of the passage to find out what he wants his readers to do.

3. What does the writer of "Fast Food for Birds" want his readers to do?

    _____

    _____

    _____

TIP 3: Writers use facts that can be checked.

A **fact** is information that can be checked to see if it is right or wrong. Here are two fact sentences:

Bicycles have two wheels.

Myron is a baker.

You can check each of these facts. You can count the number of wheels on a bicycle. You can ask Myron if he is a baker. You can even watch him bake. These facts can be checked by different people to see if they are right or wrong.

Here is a fact from the passage, "Fast Food for Birds."

Woodpeckers eat bugs.

This can be checked. You can watch a nature video, look in a book, or watch birds to see for yourself. Here is another fact:

Owls hunt in the dark.

This information can be checked, too. You can watch for owls hunting at night.

4. Now, look for another fact from the passage. Make sure that the fact can be checked. Write it on the lines below.

_____

_____

_____

_____

TIP 4: Writers sometimes tell you their opinions.

An **opinion** tells how someone feels about something. An opinion cannot be checked to see if it is right or wrong. Different people can have very different feelings about the same thing. Your opinion might not be the same as the writer's opinion. That's okay.

Sometimes just one word in a sentence will tell us that it is an opinion. Here are some common opinion words:

best	worst	funny	fun
scary	nice	mean	lucky
easy	hard	near	far
quiet	loud	pretty	ugly

Each of these opinion words may mean something different to every person.

5. Draw a line under the opinion word in the next sentence.

    Fresh fruit is the best kind of snack.

The writer thinks fresh fruit is the best kind of snack. Not everyone thinks so. Some people like cereal better. Others like milk. Maybe you think jelly sandwiches are the best kind of snack. The word *best* tells us that the sentence is an opinion.

6. Draw a line under the opinion word in the next sentence.

    Bicycles are hard to ride.

Do you think bicycles are hard to ride? Some people do. Other people think they're easy to ride. *Hard* and *easy* are opinion words.

Now let's read some opinions from "Fast Food for Birds."

7. Draw a line under the opinion word in the next sentence.

    It's fun to watch robins find their breakfast.

Some readers might not have fun watching robins find their breakfast. Other readers might. The word *fun* is an opinion word. Different people think different things are fun.

TIP 5: Opinions tell us how a writer thinks and feels.

We can't always tell how writers feel when they give only facts. It is easier to know what writers think when they tell us their opinions. Opinion words help us get to know the writer.

8. Read these sentences from "Fast Food for Birds." Draw a line under words that help you know how the writer feels.

    Birds are messy eaters. They drop parts of seeds on the floor. Too bad you will have to sweep the floor a lot!

9. What does the writer think about sweeping floors?

    _____

    _____

    _____

Reading Practice

Directions: Read the passage. Then answer Numbers 1 through 8.

How Fresh Milk Gets to You

by Winnie Lujack

If you think the story of milk begins at the store, you will have to think again. You may buy it at the store. But it goes through many steps on its way from the farm to the store.

Cows are big, beautiful animals. They eat a lot of food. Each cow eats 80 pounds of food every day. They eat grass, hay, corn, and other grains. Some cows even eat breakfast cereal, potato chips, and other "people food." Places that make these foods often have extra food they cannot sell. This food is sometimes fed to cows.

The food and water that cows eat help them make milk. Cows don't start giving milk until after they have a baby cow. The baby cow drinks its mother's milk.

Two or three times each day, dairy cows go into a barn. A machine milks the cows. The milk goes into a big tank. The tank makes the milk cold. Then it is put into a big, shiny truck. The truck takes the milk to another building. People there get it ready to go to the store.

First, people do tests to make sure the milk is safe to drink. Then they heat up the milk and quickly make it cold again. This helps keep it safe, too. Next, much of the milk goes into jugs, bottles, and cartons. Some of the milk is made into ice cream. Ice cream always tastes great! Some of it goes into butter and yogurt. Some of it goes into yummy cheeses.

Cows are very busy. They give us lots of milk each year. The next time you drink milk, remember those hard-working cows and farmers.

1. What was the writer's purpose?

   Ⓐ to tell a story about a truck driver

   Ⓑ to get the reader to buy a cow

   Ⓒ to tell about where milk comes from

2. Which of the following sentences tells an opinion?

   Ⓐ Cows are big, beautiful animals.

   Ⓑ The baby cow drinks its mother's milk.

   Ⓒ The truck takes the milk to another building.

3. Which "people food" is fed to cows?

   Ⓐ potato chips

   Ⓑ chocolate cake

   Ⓒ peanut butter

4. Read the sentence from the passage.

   Places that make these foods often have <u>extra</u> food they cannot sell.

   What is the meaning of the word *extra*?

   Ⓐ unsafe

   Ⓑ left over

   Ⓒ colorful

5. When milk goes into the tank, what happens to it first?

   Ⓐ It is put into a shiny truck.

   Ⓑ People make ice cream with it.

   Ⓒ The tank makes it cold.

6. Which of the following sentences does not contain an opinion word?

   Ⓐ Some of it goes into yummy cheeses.

   Ⓑ Each cow eats 80 pounds of food every day.

   Ⓒ Ice cream always tastes great!

7. What does the writer think about cows?

   Ⓐ She doesn't say what she thinks about cows.

   Ⓑ She thinks cows are scary.

   Ⓒ She thinks cows work very hard to give us milk.

8. Which word is made from two smaller words?

   Ⓐ potato

   Ⓑ corner

   Ⓒ cannot

Lesson 13: All About Books

There are lots of books out there. There are books that tell you stories. There are books that tell you how to do things. There are books that tell you about new things. Sometimes it can be hard to find the kind of book you want.

Some parts of books can help you find out what book is right for you. In this lesson, you'll learn about three important parts of books.

 TIP 1: Titles help you find the right book.

When Jason and Melissa went to the library, they looked for books about fish. They found lots of books with the word *fish* in the title. "I can't read all of these books!" Jason said. "I just want a book that will tell me how to care for pet fish."

Melissa said, "You can tell which book to pick by reading the titles. Titles are like road signs that point you in the right direction."

Look at this list of titles to help Jason find the right book.

Fishing in the United States

Space Fish from Planet X

Taking Care of Pet Fish

Justin's Fish Cookbook

One of these titles looks like the name of a storybook. Another seems to be about how to cook fish. Only one of these books will have the information Jason wants.

1. Which book would teach Jason about raising fish in a fish tank?

   A. *Fishing in the United States*

   B. *Taking Care of Pet Fish*

   C. *Space Fish from Planet X*

2. Which book would tell how to cook fish?

   A. *Fishing in the United States*

   B. *Taking Care of Pet Fish*

   C. *Justin's Fish Cookbook*

3. Which book is probably a made-up story?

   A. *Space Fish from Planet X*

   B. *Fishing in the United States*

   C. *Taking Care of Pet Fish*

You already know that reading the title helps you know what a book is about. Now let's look at how you can find information in a book.

TIP 2: Some books have chapters.

Chapters are smaller parts of a book. Sometimes each chapter has a different title. Each chapter tells part of the book's story or gives part of the book's information.

A book title tells you what a book is about. A chapter title tells you what a chapter is about.

 TIP 3: A table of contents tells you what is in the book.

A **table of contents** gives a list of the different chapters in a book. It is found near the front of most books. It also gives a page number for each chapter.

Let's read more about Jason and Melissa.

At the library, Jason and Melissa found many books about fish. They picked one book that looked very interesting. That book was *Taking Care of Pet Fish* by Alice Smith. Jason and Melissa opened the book to its table of contents.

This is what the table of contents looked like:

Table of Contents	
Having Fish of Your Own	5
Choosing Your Fish	13
Feeding Your Fish	17

As you read the chapter titles, you can tell where to find the information you're looking for. Each chapter title has a page number with it.

Help Jason find the information he needs by answering these questions about the table of contents from *Taking Care of Pet Fish*.

4. Jason isn't sure about what kind of fish he wants. On which page can he find help?

   A. 5

   B. 13

   C. 17

5. Jason wants to find out what it will be like to have his own fish. To which page should he turn?

   A. 5

   B. 13

   C. 17

6. Which chapter should Jason read to find out what his fish will eat?

   A. Having Fish of Your Own

   B. Choosing Your Fish

   C. Feeding Your Fish

7. What chapter title would Jason find on page 13?

   A. Having Fish of Your Own

   B. Choosing Your Fish

   C. Feeding Your Fish

Reading Practice

Directions: Read the paragraph. Then answer Numbers 1 through 5.

Sara loves to go for walks in the woods with her grandfather. She also loves to read about the things she sees on their walks. They see lots of different animals. They see people fishing at the lake. They also see lots of insects. Insects are bugs. Sara went to the library. Here are some of the books she found:

1. Which of these books will probably have information about the different bugs Sara sees?

    Ⓐ *Fishing in the United States*

    Ⓑ *All About Insects*

    Ⓒ *A Rabbit's Life in Winter*

2. Which word has the same sound as the underlined letter in *life*?

    Ⓐ miss

    Ⓑ ride

    Ⓒ train

3. Which book most likely tells us about what rabbits do when it is cold outside?

   Ⓐ *Fishing in the United States*

   Ⓑ *All About Insects*

   Ⓒ *A Rabbit's Life in Winter*

4. Sara wants to know if the animal she saw today was a fox. She is looking at the table of contents for *Animals of the United States.* On what page should she start looking for a picture of a fox?

Table of Contents

The Secret Life of Bears 3

Bugs, Fish, and Birds 9

Beavers, Foxes, and Other Furry Animals 17

   Ⓐ 3

   Ⓑ 9

   Ⓒ 17

5. Which word has a suffix?

   Ⓐ fishing

   Ⓑ rabbit

   Ⓒ insects

Lesson 14: Reading Pictures

Did you know that you can read a picture? You can. In fact, pictures and drawings can be fun to read. They can show us important things. They can also show information in ways that make it easy to understand.

In this lesson, you will learn to work with graphs and drawings.

 TIP 1: A picture graph uses pictures to show information.

A **graph** is a drawing that helps show information. There are lots of kinds of graphs. **Picture graphs** use pictures to show information. Each picture shows you how much of something there is.

Look at this picture graph. It shows what kinds of vegetables Farmer Bob sold at his vegetable stand.

Kinds	Bags of Vegetables Sold
Tomatoes	🍅🍅🍅🍅🍅🍅
Carrots	🥕🥕🥕🥕🥕
Corn	🌽🌽🌽

Key: Each Picture = One Bag

1. What kinds of vegetables did Farmer Bob sell?

_____

_____

_____

The picture graph also shows how many bags of vegetables Farmer Bob sold. Each little picture stands for one bag of vegetables. Each tomato means he sold one bag of tomatoes.

2. Which vegetable did Farmer Bob sell the most bags of? (Remember that each picture stands for one bag of that kind of vegetable.)

   A. tomatoes

   B. carrots

   C. corn

3. Which vegetable did Farmer Bob sell the fewest bags of?

   A. tomatoes

   B. carrots

   C. corn

4. How many bags of carrots did Farmer Bob sell?

   A. 3

   B. 5

   C. 6

TIP 2: A circle graph looks like a pie.

Think of a pie that has been cut into pieces, or slices. You might take one slice of pie. Your dad might take two slices. It probably won't be too long before the whole pie is gone!

A **circle graph** looks like a pie. Each piece shows you how much of something there is. **Pie chart** is another name for a circle graph.

Miss Williams took her second-grade class to the library. While there, each person checked out one book.

This pie chart shows that some of the class checked out storybooks, some checked out picture books, and some checked out books of poems.

Books Checked Out

The size of each piece of pie tells you more information about the people in the class. Bigger pieces of pie mean more people checked out those books. Smaller pieces of pie mean fewer people checked out those books.

5. Which kind of book did the most people check out?

    A. storybook

    B. picture book

    C. book of poems

6. Which kind of book did the fewest people check out?

    A. storybook

    B. picture book

    C. book of poems

7. Which kind of book did none of the people check out?

    A. storybook

    B. picture book

    C. joke book

Standards and Skills: 3.6

TIP 3: A diagram shows the names of the different parts.

A **diagram** is a picture or drawing of something that tells the names of its parts.

When you see a baseball bat, you probably know what to call it. But you probably don't know the right names of all the bat's parts.

One way to learn the names of those parts is to look at a diagram. Here are two pictures. One is a diagram of a baseball bat. The other is a picture a batter. Look at the two pictures. Then answer Numbers 8 and 9.

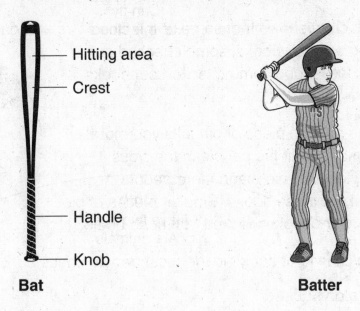

Bat   **Batter**

8. Which part of a bat does the batter hold?

   A. handle

   B. knob

   C. crest

9. Which part of a bat is biggest?

   A. knob

   B. handle

   C. hitting area

TIP 4: Some pictures show you how things are the same and different.

There are all kinds of pictures that give information.

Another kind of picture shows you how two things are the same and different. Look at the next picture. It shows two circles. The circles help show how birds and fish are the same and different.

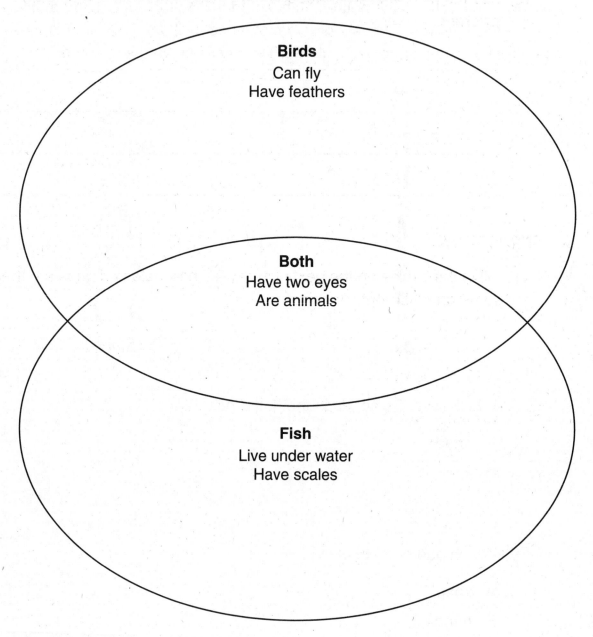

Standards and Skills: 3.6

The place where the two circles touch is for information about how the two things are the same. Both birds and fish have two eyes. Both birds and fish are animals.

The places where the two circles are not together show how the two things are different. Birds have feathers. Fish do not. Birds can fly. Fish cannot.

10. Use the picture to write about another way that birds and fish are different.

____

____

____

____

Now you try.

11. Fill in the circles on the next picture. Tell how cats and dogs are the same and different.

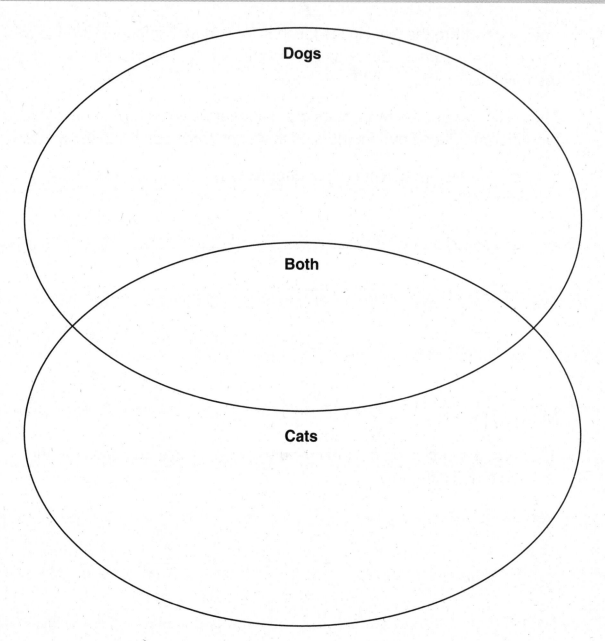

Reading Practice

Directions: Look at the graph and diagrams. Answer the questions that go with each one.

Mrs. Jewel asked her class about their pets. Then she made this picture graph to show her information to the class.

Pets Belonging to Mrs. Jewel's Class

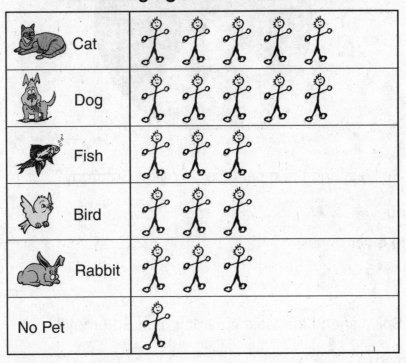

Key: 🏃 = 1 Person

1. Which pets do the most people have?

   Ⓐ dogs and fish

   Ⓑ dogs and cats

   Ⓒ dogs and birds

2. How many people have no pet?

   Ⓐ one

   Ⓑ two

   Ⓒ three

3. How many people have a rabbit as a pet?

   Ⓐ one

   Ⓑ two

   Ⓒ three

Tom made a pie chart to show what his dog Spike did on Saturday.

Spike's Saturday

4. What did Spike spend the most time doing on Saturday?

Ⓐ sleeping

Ⓑ chasing other dogs

Ⓒ eating

5. What did Spike spend the least time doing on Saturday?

Ⓐ swimming

Ⓑ sleeping

Ⓒ eating

Look at this diagram of an octopus. Then answer Number 6.

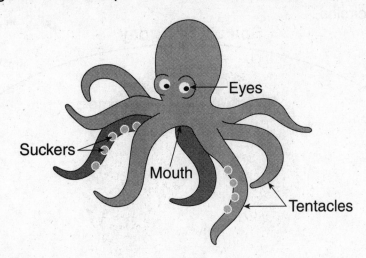

6. How many tentacles does the octopus in the diagram have?

Ⓐ two

Ⓑ five

Ⓒ eight

Greta wanted to show how the sun and the moon are the same and different. She drew these circles.

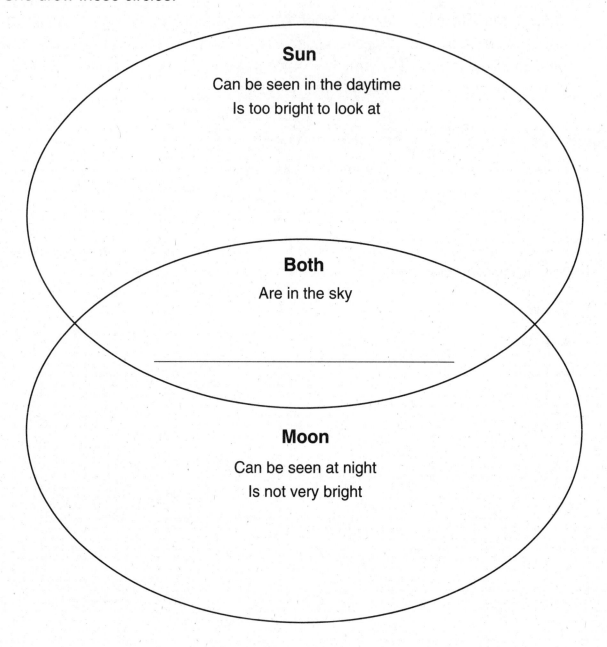

7. What should Greta write on the blank line?

    Ⓐ Can be touched

    Ⓑ Are round

    Ⓒ Have trees

Lesson 15: Maps and Directions

Maps and directions help you do things. Maps help you find your way from one place to another. Directions show you how to do something. They can tell you how to cook something. They can tell you how to make something. They can tell you how to do almost anything!

 TIP 1: Maps are small drawings of places.

Maps are drawings. They show big places on small pieces of paper. Most maps show rivers, roads, lakes, towns, airports, and so on. There are maps of parks, towns, states, countries, and even maps of the world.

Here is a map of Oaktown. Look at it carefully. Then answer the questions.

Oaktown

I. Which street must Jim cross to get from his house to the park?

A. Oak Street

B. Main Street

C. Blue Street

2. Which street is between Tanya's house and Jim's house?

    A. East Street

    B. Main Street

    C. Blue Street

3. Which street is between the school and the store?

    A. Main Street

    B. Blue Street

    C. Oak Street

4. Which streets does Ty cross to get from his house to the swimming pool?

    A. Blue Street and Main Street

    B. East Street and Blue Street

    C. Blue Street and Oak Street

5. Which of the following is closest to the playground?

    A. the park

    B. the school

    C. the store

TIP 2: Follow directions step by step.

Directions often have steps. **Steps** tell you what to do. When following the steps to make or do something, don't forget these three rules:

- First, read each step all the way through before you begin.

- Second, go get everything you need and have it ready before you start.

- Third, follow each step in order.

Here are the steps you need to follow to wash your bike.

How to Wash Your Bike

Things needed: bucket, spoon, water, dish soap, rag, bike

Directions:
Step 1: Put a spoonful of dish soap in the bottom of the bucket.
Step 2: Fill the bucket with water.
Step 3: Get the rag wet.
Step 4: Clean the handle bars, seat, and frame of your bike.

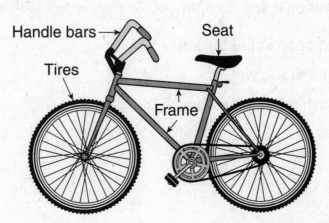

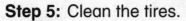

Handle bars →

Seat

Tires

Frame

Step 5: Clean the tires.
Step 6: Dump out the soapy water and fill the bucket with clean water.
Step 7: Rinse the soap off your bike with the rag and clean water.

Step 8: Let your bike dry in the sun.

6. How much soap should you put in the bucket?

   A. a whole bottle

   B. a cupful

   C. a spoonful

7. What should you do after you fill the bucket with water?

   A. put soap in the bucket

   B. get the rag wet

   C. wash the handle bars

Reading Practice

Directions: Use the following map to answer Numbers 1 through 3.

Sparkle Lake

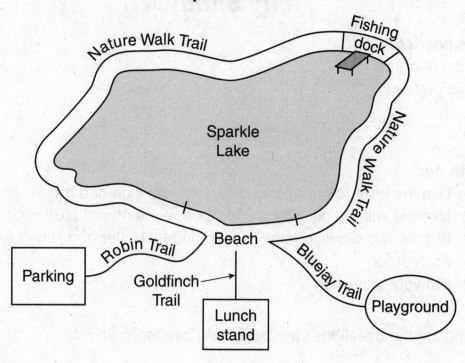

1. What trail should you take to get from the beach to the lunch stand?

   Ⓐ Robin Trail

   Ⓑ Goldfinch Trail

   Ⓒ Bluejay Trail

2. What trail should you take to get from the fishing dock to the beach?

   Ⓐ Nature Walk Trail

   Ⓑ Robin Trail

   Ⓒ Goldfinch Trail

3. What trail goes around the whole lake?

   Ⓐ Robin Trail

   Ⓑ Bluejay Trail

   Ⓒ Nature Walk Trail

Read the following directions. Then answer Numbers 4 and 5.

How to Make a Peanut Butter and Jelly Sandwich

Things needed:
- 2 slices of bread
- peanut butter
- jelly
- a knife

What to do:

Step 1: Use the knife to put peanut butter on one side of a bread slice.

Step 2: Use the knife to put jelly on one side of the other bread slice.

Step 3: Put the two slices together so the peanut butter and jelly are stuck to each other.

Step 4: Eat your sandwich.

4. What do the directions say you should use the knife for?

   Ⓐ to cut the sandwich

   Ⓑ to put peanut butter and jelly on the bread

   Ⓒ to open the jar of jelly

5. What should you do after you put the two slices together?

   Ⓐ put peanut butter on one side of a bread slice

   Ⓑ put jelly on one side of another bread slice

   Ⓒ Eat your sandwich.

Unit 3

Understanding Stories and Poems

What kind of stories do you like best? Scary stories? Animal stories? Stories about friends? Do you like to make up your own stories or read stories written by someone else?

This unit will help you see what makes a good story. You will learn about characters, setting, and plot. You'll also learn about poems. Poems can also tell stories. Once you've learned all about stories, you might want to write one of your own. Go ahead . . . tell me a story!

In This Unit

Tell Me a Story

Stories Side By Side

Words That Sing

Learning to Listen

Lesson 16: Tell Me a Story

There are lots of different stories to read and listen to. You probably know lots of stories already. Maybe you've made up some of your own stories. In this lesson, you'll learn about the two main kinds of stories.

 TIP 1: There are two kinds of stories.

There are made-up stories and true stories. **Made-up stories** are not real. They never really happened. **True stories** are about real people, real things, and real events.

Made-Up Story

True Story

A book about monsters from space is made up. A book that tells how to study the stars is about a real thing.

Made-Up Story

True Story

The story of Jack and the Beanstalk is made up. A story that tells how
to plant beans is about real things.

If a story tells true facts about real things and people, it is a true story.

1. Which of these books is about a real thing?

   A. *Tony the Singing Goldfish*

   B. *How to Fly a Kite*

   C. *The Ghost and the Magic Cat*

2. Which of the following is probably a made-up story?

   A. *All About Rivers in the United States*

   B. *Fun Games to Play After School*

   C. *The Monkey That Lives in My Hat*

 TIP 2: The characters are the people or animals in a story.

Characters are the people or animals things happen to. They are the people or animals in the story. Little Red Riding Hood is a character. The big bad wolf is a character, too.

Getting to know the characters can be fun. Ask yourself lots of questions about the characters. It will help you find details about them in the story. Details can tell you what the characters look like, how they think, and how they act.

Read the story below. Watch for the details. Then answer Numbers 3 and 4.

Uncle Charlie is tall and thin. When he sits down, his arms and legs fold up like a folding chair. Uncle Charlie has a shiny pink head and a little ring of hair just above his ears. He says he grew so fast that he pushed his head up through his hair. Uncle Charlie likes to laugh. He's always happy. He makes me happy when I'm with him.

Uncle Willie is short and round. When he sits in our big stuffed chair, his feet barely touch the floor. Uncle Willie has snow-white hair. He is very quiet and doesn't laugh much. When he does laugh, his face gets as red as a fire truck. Most of the time I can't tell if Uncle Willie is happy or sad.

3. Which drawing looks the most like Uncle Charlie?

A.   B.   C.

4. Which word best tells about Uncle Willie?

A. quiet

B. angry

C. cheerful

TIP 3: The setting is where and when a story happens.

The **setting** is the time and place in which a story happens. The setting of a story might be a roller rink on a Monday night. Every story has a setting. Long stories and books may have many different settings. If you read the details carefully, they will tell you when and where each part of the story takes place.

Read the following two stories about a park and a beach. Then answer Numbers 5 through 8.

Sunnyside State Park

The gate to Sunnyside State Park was closed and locked. Morning sunlight peeked through the tall trees. Flowers were starting to open up to the sun. A warm wind blew through the playground. It was early, and the park was empty.

Sandy Beach

Sandy Beach was crawling with people. Some splashed in the water. Some played games. Others lay on bright beach towels and slept in the afternoon sunlight. A man in a large white hat sold balloons to the children. Every now and then a child's balloon would get away, floating up into the clear summer sky.

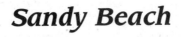

5. What is the setting for the first story?

    A. a park

    B. a farm

    C. a lake

6. When does the first story take place?

    A. winter

    B. spring

    C. fall

7. Which is one way "Sunnyside State Park" is different from "Sandy Beach"?

    A. The park is empty, but the beach is crowded.

    B. The park is open, but the beach is closed.

    C. There are balloons in the park, but there are towels at the beach.

8. During what time of year does the second story take place?

    A. fall

    B. spring

    C. summer

TIP 4: The plot is what happens in the story.

The **plot** tells what happens and why it happens. **Events** are the things that happen.

Most stories have a beginning, a middle, and an end.

- The **beginning** tells about the characters and the setting. It also tells about the problems the characters must solve.

- The **middle** tells how the characters try to solve the problems.

- The **end** tells how the problems are solved.

One character might have a problem with another character. That other character might be a parent, a neighbor, or a big bad wolf.

The problem could be with a thing. The thing could be a snowstorm, a flat tire, or a rocky hill.

Sometimes, a character has a problem within himself or herself. A child might want to be brave in the dark. Or, a walker might need to pick a path to take.

Read this story about a boy who loved trains. Look for Michael's problem.

The Boy Who Loved Trains
by Nikki Lake

Michael loved trains. He had wooden trains, plastic trains, paper trains, and wind-up trains. But Michael wanted another kind of train. Michael wanted a train that could run on its own. He wanted the one he had seen at Toy City. It had seven cars and a flashing light. The train could make real puffs of smoke as it went along the track.

"You already have too many trains," Michael's father said. But Michael didn't think he had too many trains.

"One train is as good as another," his mother said.

But one train wasn't as good as another to Michael.

No one understood how much Michael wanted that train.

Then one day Michael's grandfather came to visit. He gave Michael a large box.

Sometimes, it's fun to think ahead while you're reading. Let's try that now.

9. What do you think is in the box that Michael's grandfather gives Michael?

_____

_____

_____

_____

Now, read the rest of the story to see if you were right.

Michael set his trains on the floor and took the box. He could feel something moving inside. Then he saw a wet nose pushing through one of the air holes in the lid. He opened the box. Inside was a brown puppy. Michael gave his grandfather a big hug and thanked him. Then he ran outside with his furry new friend. He left his trains on the floor behind him.

10. Did you guess correctly or did the writer fool you?

_____

_____

_____

11. What is Michael's main problem in the story?

    A. He does not like trains anymore.

    B. He wants a train that can run on its own.

    C. He thinks he has too many trains.

12. What problem does Michael's father have in the story?

    A. He thinks Michael has too many trains.

    B. He doesn't like trains that puff smoke.

    C. He thinks trains cost too much money.

13. When does Michael's grandfather give him the puppy?

    A. at the beginning of the story

    B. in the middle of the story

    C. at the end of the story

Reading Practice

Directions: Read the story. Then answer Numbers 1 through 8.

Marvin's Ride

by Natalie Miller

Marvin peeked from his mouse hole in the wall at 444 Daisy Drive. The little girl was skateboarding in the front hall again. Oh, boy! Marvin wanted to skateboard more than anything.

One day while the little girl was at school, Marvin called his friends. They pushed the girl's bright red skateboard into the driveway. Marvin jumped on and yelled, "Give me a BIG PUSH, please!" So, Marvin's little mouse friends did just that. Marvin shot down the driveway and flew into the street.

The skateboard tore down Daisy Drive. "Oh, nooo!" Marvin screamed.

"Where are the brakes?" Marvin cried. He skated past a stop sign and ran right into a mail carrier. Letters flew into the air like snowflakes.

Marvin shut his eyes tightly. He was going faster and faster. The skateboard zoomed through the open doorway of Sid's Bowl-A-Rama.

Marvin opened his eyes. He was sailing down a bowling alley. He was headed straight for 10 huge pins. He was lined up perfectly. CRASH! BOOM! BANG! Pins flew wildly in every direction.

Marvin hung on for dear life as an angry man threw the skateboard out the back door. He climbed on top of the board just as it hit a bump and crashed.

"The skateboard is a mess," Marvin cried. "How will I get home? Oh, dear!"

Marvin slowly walked back to 444 Daisy Drive. He called his little mouse friends together. They helped him push and pull and tug the little girl's skateboard home.

Afterward, Marvin crawled into his hole in the wall. He needed rest. He needed to think. Marvin lay on his tiny mouse bed for three hours. Then he made a choice. From now on, he would stay away from all things with wheels.

And that is just what Marvin did.

1. Where does this story begin?

   Ⓐ on Fourth Street

   Ⓑ at 444 Daisy Drive

   Ⓒ in Sid's Bowl-A-Rama

2. Which of these events happens first?

   Ⓐ Marvin gets thrown out the back door.

   Ⓑ Marvin rolls through Sid's Bowl-A-Rama.

   Ⓒ Marvin runs into a mail carrier.

3. What causes Marvin to cry out, "Where are the brakes?"

   Ⓐ He can't stop the skateboard.

   Ⓑ He wants to stop at Sid's Bowl-A-Rama.

   Ⓒ He needs to get back to Daisy Drive.

4. Which of the following best tells about Marvin's ride?

   Ⓐ He has a wild ride on a skateboard.

   Ⓑ He runs into a mail carrier.

   Ⓒ He crashes into 10 bowling pins.

5. What is Marvin's main problem in the story?

   Ⓐ A man gets angry with him.

   Ⓑ His friends won't help him.

   Ⓒ He can't stop the skateboard.

6. Which of these is a setting from "Marvin's Ride"?

   Ⓐ a hole in the wall

   Ⓑ a kitchen counter

   Ⓒ a shelf at a toy store

7. Why will Marvin probably stay away from roller skates?

   Ⓐ because he's afraid of falling

   Ⓑ because they are too large for a mouse

   Ⓒ because they have wheels

8. Which word best tells about Marvin?

   Ⓐ mean

   Ⓑ scared

   Ⓒ big

Lesson 17: Stories Side By Side

People from around the world are different from each other. They wear different clothes. They eat different foods. They play different games. They speak different languages.

But people in every country have the same need for food, a home, safety, happiness, and love. They also share a need to make the world a better place.

In this lesson, you will learn how the same kinds of stories are told in many different lands.

 TIP 1: The same story can be told in many ways.

Many of the same stories have been told in different countries for thousands of years.

Most of these stories were told before people knew how to read and write. The stories were not written down. That's why they changed over the years as they passed from one country to another.

Have you ever played the game "Telephone"? To play, everyone sits in a circle. The first person whispers something to the next person. That person whispers the same thing to the next person. By the time the sentence gets around the circle, it is usually very different! The same thing happens with stories. As people tell them to each other, they change.

There are more than 1,000 different ways to tell the story we know as "Cinderella."

Why do you think the story of Cinderella might be told differently in different countries?

_____

_____

_____

_____

 TIP 2: The main idea often stays the same.

In Lesson 8, you learned about the main idea. The **main idea** is what the story is mostly about. When you read the same story by two different people, the main idea of each story is often the same.

Many countries may have stories that are like our story about Cinderella. The main idea is that a poor girl finds someone who helps her go to a special dance. The dance changes her life.

This part of the story stays the same most of the time.

TIP 3: Compare the characters, setting, and events of the stories.

To **compare** means to show how things are the same and different. To compare two stories, see if both stories have the same characters, setting, and events.

In Iraq, people tell a story about a girl called Maha. This story is a lot like the Cinderella story you might know. But there are differences. Maha is the daughter of a fisherman. A magic fish makes her a dress so she can go to a party.

There is an American Indian story from the Zuni tribe that is also like the Cinderella story. The American Indian story is about a girl named Turkey Girl. In this story, turkeys make a girl a new robe and soft shoes so that she can go to the Corn Dance.

In both of these stories, the main idea is the same. It is the details that change. The characters have different names. They live in different places. And, the events are a little different.

 TIP 4: Think about why each writer wrote the story.

Find the main idea of each story. What is the writer trying to teach you? Do the stories teach the same lesson? Do they teach different lessons? How are the lessons in the two stories the same and different?

Reading Practice

Directions: Read the passages. Then answer Numbers 1 through 6.

Rosy

a Cinderella story from Egypt
retold by Alicia Monroe

Once upon a time, a girl named Rosy lived along the Nile River. Rosy lived in a land of mighty kings. She was a servant. She cooked and cleaned for people.

Rosy's only friend was a great bird that circled above her. The bird listened to her songs and watched her dance.

One day, the bird flew out of the sky and took one of Rosy's shoes. It flew to the palace of the king and dropped the shoe into his lap. "This is a good sign," said the king. "Every girl in my kingdom will try this shoe. The girl who can wear this shoe will be my queen."

The king's great boat floated up the Nile River. The king had been searching for a queen for weeks. But he could find no one. Just as the boat was turning to go back, the king saw Rosy dancing on the bank of the river. "You must try this shoe," he called. Sure enough, the shoe fit.

"I have found my queen," said the king.

"But she is a servant girl," said a prince. "She can only cook and clean."

"She was once a servant," the king said, "but from now on, she will be your queen."

Tam

a Cinderella story from Vietnam
retold by Rick Zollo

In the Land of the Dragon lived a kind and gentle girl named Tam. When Tam's mother died, her father married again. Tam's new mother and stepsister Cam were very mean to Tam.

One day, Tam caught a small fish. She took it home and kept it in a bowl of water. She grew to love the little fish. When her stepsister saw this, she cooked the fish and ate it.

Tam found the fish bones and put them under her sleeping mat. During the night, the bones turned into a pair of jeweled shoes. One day, as Tam played barefoot along the river, a tiger took one of the shoes. He carried it to the gates of the palace where the prince found it. "I must meet the girl who owns this shoe," the prince said.

All of the girls in the land came to try on the jeweled shoe. Cam and her mother went. They left Tam at home to pick rice.

But the tiger returned to Tam and said, "Leave the rice. Climb on my back."

They ran silently through rice fields and forests until they reached the palace.

The prince slipped the jeweled shoe onto Tam's foot. It fit perfectly. The prince looked into Tam's eyes. Then he called her "princess" and asked her to be his wife.

1. Which character in "Rosy" is most like the tiger in "Tam"?

   Ⓐ Rosy

   Ⓑ the king

   Ⓒ the great bird

2. Where does the story "Rosy" take place?

   Ⓐ along the Nile River

   Ⓑ in the Land of the Dragon

   Ⓒ at the prince's house

3. Which of these is a setting from the story "Tam"?

   Ⓐ a shoe store

   Ⓑ the prince's palace

   Ⓒ the kitchen at Tam's house

4. Which of these animals helps Tam get jeweled shoes?

   Ⓐ a fish

   Ⓑ a frog

   Ⓒ a bird

5. What kind of a person is Tam?

   Ⓐ kind

   Ⓑ unloving

   Ⓒ mean

6. Which sentence tells how the two stories are the same and different?

   Ⓐ The settings, characters, and events are very different.

   Ⓑ The settings and characters are the same, but the events are different.

   Ⓒ The stories have almost the same events but different settings and characters.

Lesson 18: Words That Sing

Songs are poems set to music.

But did you know that many poems can "sing" without music?

This lesson will show you how poems use words to "sing" us a song. It will also show you how poems can paint pictures in our minds. Most of all, it will show you how poems can be fun to read.

Read "The Blanket Tent." It will help you understand this lesson.

The Blanket Tent
by Mike Acton

How we love the smell of a summer's day
In the shade of our blanket tent
Where we've flattened the yellow dandelions
And rolled till the grass is bent.

We pretend to go on safari trips
And to camp along jungle streams
Where we listen to bright-colored birds that call
To us through a vine-covered dream.

Or sometimes we camp in the Arctic ice,
Where it's fifty degrees below,
And we shiver and shake in our blanket tent
While our sled dogs sleep in the snow.

But sometimes we play at nothing at all.
We just lie on our backs and stare
At the ragged old blanket above us,
Which shelters the worlds we share.

TIP 1: Read the poem again and again.

Poets write about things they have seen and heard. They want you to see and hear those same things when you read their poems.

Read "The Blanket Tent" one more time. Let the words make pictures in your mind as you read.

Do you see how the poem is written in groups of four lines? A **stanza** is a group of lines.

After you have finished reading the poem, draw a picture about something from the second or third stanza. Draw your picture in the box below.

1.

TIP 2: Listen for the music of the poem.

Some poems make music with words. You hear a musical beat because of how the poets say things.

You have heard the music of poetry ever since you were a baby. Before you could read you may have heard such rhymes as this:

Five Little Monkeys
a Nursery Rhyme

Five little monkeys jumping on the bed
one fell off and bumped his head.
Momma called the doctor and the doctor said,
"No more monkeys jumping on the bed!"

Four little monkeys jumping on the bed
one fell off and bumped his head.
Momma called the doctor and the doctor said,
"No more monkeys jumping on the bed!"

Three little monkeys jumping on the bed
one fell off and bumped his head.
Momma called the doctor and the doctor said,
"No more monkeys jumping on the bed!"

Two little monkeys jumping on the bed
one fell off and bumped his head.
Momma called the doctor and the doctor said,
"No more monkeys jumping on the bed!"

One little monkey jumping on the bed
one fell off and bumped his head.
Momma called the doctor and the doctor said,
"No more monkeys jumping on the bed!"

Can you hear the musical beat in the poem above? This is called **rhythm**.

Follow along as your teacher reads "Choosing Shoes." Listen to the music that the words make with their rhythm.

Choosing Shoes

New shoes, new shoes,
   Red and pink and blue shoes.
Tell me, what would you choose,
   If they'd let us buy?

Buckle shoes, bow shoes,
   Pretty pointy-toe shoes,
Strappy, cappy low shoes;
   Let's have some to try.

Bright shoes, white shoes,
   Dandy-dance-by-night shoes,
Perhaps a little tight shoes,
   Like some? So would I.

But

Flat shoes, fat shoes,
   Stump-along-like-that shoes,
Wipe-them-on-the-mat shoes,
   That's the sort they'll buy.

TIP 3: Watch and listen for words that rhyme.

Rhyming words are words that have the same sound. Many poems have words that sound the same at the ends of lines. Here are some examples of rhyming words:

hat / cat

bed / head

you / through

box / fox

go / snow

In "Choosing Shoes" on page 157, the words *shoes* and *choose* are rhyming words.

2. What other rhyming words can you find in "Choosing Shoes"?

_____

3. Write a rhyming word for each of the following:

blue _____

day _____

tree _____

fly _____

A **poet** is someone who writes poems. Help the poet of the next poem by circling the correct rhyming words to finish this poem.

If You Are Looking for a Mouse

If you are looking for a mouse
Don't try to find one in my _____.

(tree / house / shoe)

The mouse that lived here ran away
When Tom the cat came here to _____.

(stay / sleep / live)

TIP 4: Look for the main idea in the poem.

Poems are like other kinds of writing. They tell things that happen. They tell about feelings. They can be scary or happy or sad. Every poem has some kind of main idea.

When you first read a poem, you may not understand every word. Just try to find out what the poem is mainly about. Then read the poem again to be sure about what each line means.

Read the next poem carefully. Think about what the poem is mainly about.

Old Mother Duck

by Robyn Winchell

Old mother duck walked down the road,
Three ducklings in the back.
They waddled close behind her
Saying quack, quack, quack.

They followed her across the lawn
And down the garden path,
And when she slid into the pond
They followed—splash, splash, splash.

4. What is this poem mostly about?

   A. three little ducks crossing the lawn

   B. three little ducks splashing in the pond

   C. three little ducks following their mother

Reading Practice

Directions: Read the poem. Then answer Numbers 1 through 5.

Ladybugs and Tumblebugs

by Mickey Toom

I spent most all of yesterday
Behind the poplar trees
And crawling through the hollyhocks
On busy hands and knees.

I saw a hundred moving things!
You wouldn't think there'd be
So many funny-looking bugs
That creeped around like me.

I couldn't tell by watching them
Exactly what they did,
Or where they went as they passed by,
Or why they sometimes hid.

hollyhocks

I saw ladybugs and tumblebugs—
Green bugs, red, and brown—
Giant bugs and tiny bugs,
And bugs that flew around.

I splashed back again this morning
To the poplar trees to see
If the busy bugs of yesterday
Would still remember me.

But when I reached my watching place,
There were no bugs to see.
Just raindrops sparkling on the grass
And hollyhocks—and me.

1. What is the main idea of the poem?

   Ⓐ Flowers get wet in the rain.

   Ⓑ Some bugs hide from people.

   Ⓒ A boy watches busy bugs.

2. Why are there no bugs to watch on the second day?

   Ⓐ The rain made the bugs hide.

   Ⓑ The bugs are still asleep.

   Ⓒ It is too hot outside for the bugs.

3. In the first stanza of "Ladybugs and Tumblebugs," which words rhyme?

   Ⓐ yesterday / trees

   Ⓑ trees / knees

   Ⓒ yesterday / hollyhocks

4. Which of the following is true about the poem "Ladybugs and Tumblebugs"?

   Ⓐ The poem has three stanzas.

   Ⓑ The poem has a musical beat.

   Ⓒ The poem does not have rhyming words.

5. Read these lines from the poem.

   > But when I reached my watching place,
   > There were no bugs to see.
   > Just raindrops <u>sparkling</u> on the grass
   > And hollyhocks—and me.

   Which word means about the same as the word *sparkling*?

   Ⓐ shining

   Ⓑ shaking

   Ⓒ climbing

Standards and Skills: 2.9

Lesson 19: Learning to Listen

You can read a story by yourself. You can listen as somebody reads a story to you. Or you can watch and listen as actors present a story on television or in a movie.

You can add new words to those you already know by reading and listening to all kinds of stories and information.

In this lesson you will learn some tips for listening to a story. You'll also learn tips for writing and talking about that story.

 TIP 1: Listening is very important.

If you don't listen carefully when somebody gives you a phone number, you might write down the wrong numbers. If you don't listen carefully when your teacher tells you to read pages 4 through 6, you might end up reading pages 4 through 60. And, if you don't listen carefully when a story is being read to you, you might get the idea that a fairy godmother turned Cinderella into a big orange pumpkin!

Here are some tips to help you.

 TIP 2: Have fun listening to the story.

Have fun listening to the story as it is read to you. Pretend you are one or more of the people in the story. Look for characters and events that make you think of people or events you know about.

 TIP 3: Let the story paint pictures in your mind.

Try to picture the characters, settings, and events. The more you put yourself into the story, the better you will understand it. And, the more you understand the story, the easier it will be to talk about it and write about it.

TIP 4: Keep your mind on the story.

Do your best to listen carefully to the story. If you look out the window or start thinking about what's for supper tonight, you may miss important information.

 TIP 5: After you have heard the story, write a few notes.

Write down the names of characters, important settings, and problems the characters have. Try to write down the main idea.

Reading Practice

Directions: Listen carefully as your teacher reads you a story called "The Three Billy Goats Gruff." Use the rest of this page to make notes about the story. Then answer Numbers 1 through 4.

Notes:

1. Who are the characters in "The Three Billy Goats Gruff"?

_____

_____

_____

2. What is the setting for "The Three Billy Goats Gruff"?

   Ⓐ a house

   Ⓑ a bridge

   Ⓒ a forest

3. What problem do the three billy goats Gruff have?

   Ⓐ They need money to pay the troll.

   Ⓑ They are lost far away from home.

   Ⓒ A mean troll says he will eat them.

4. How is their problem solved?

_____

_____

_____

Appendix

Word Power Log

Activity Page

Word Power Log

Using the Word Power Log will help you become a better reader. As you come across new words, write them on the lines below. When you have time, look them up in a dictionary. Then write what they mean.

Word: _____

Meaning: _____

_____

Word: _____

Meaning: _____

_____

Word: _____

Meaning: _____

_____

Word: _____

Meaning: _____

_____

Word: _____

Meaning: _____

_____

Word: _____

Meaning: _____

_____

Word: _____

Meaning: _____

_____

Word: _____

Meaning: _____

_____

Word: _____

Meaning: _____

_____

Word: _____

Meaning: _____

_____

Word: _____

Meaning: _____

_____

Word: _____

Meaning: _____

_____

Word: _____

Meaning: _____

_____

Word: _____

Meaning: _____

_____

Word: _____

Meaning: _____

_____

Word: _____

Meaning: _____

_____

Word: _____

Meaning: _____

_____

Word: _____

Meaning: _____

_____

Word: _____

Meaning: _____

_____

Word: _____

Meaning: _____

_____

Activity Page

Use with pages 86 and 87.